Instructor's Guide to Accompany
DC/AC Circuits and Electronics:
Principles & Applications

Robert J. Herrick
Purdue University
West Lafayette, Indiana

THOMSON

DELMAR LEARNING   Australia Canada Mexico Singapore Spain United Kingdom United States

THOMSON

DELMAR LEARNING

Instructor's Guide to Accompany DC/AC Circuits and Electronics: Principles & Applications

By Robert J. Herrick

Executive Director:
Alar Elken

Executive Editor:
Sandy Clark

Senior Acquisitions Editor:
Gregory L. Clayton

Senior Development Editor:
Michelle Ruelos Cannistraci

Executive Marketing Manager:
Maura Theriault

Channel Manager:
Fair Huntoon

Marketing Coordinator:
Brian McGrath

Executive Production Manager:
Mary Ellen Black

Production Manager:
Larry Main

Senior Project Editor:
Christopher Chien

Art/Design Coordinator:
David Arsenault

Technology Project Manager:
David Porush

Technology Project Specialist:
Kevin Smith

Senior Editorial Assistant:
Dawn Daugherty

Library of Congress Cataloging-in-Publication Data:

ISBN: 1-4018-5253-X

NOTICE TO THE READER

Contents

Preface

This instructor's guide is provided to aid the instructor in following the major steps required to solve the problems in the textbook *DC/AC Circuits and Electronics: Principles & Applications* by Robert J. Herrick.

Chapter Overview

Chapter 1. Units and Number Notation: This chapter provides essential standard unit and number notation concepts and terminology.

Chapter 2. Current, Voltage, and Common: This chapter provides basic terminology and understanding of current and voltage. A *foundational approach* to circuit notation and analysis is emphasized. Fixed dc voltage supplies, current meters, and voltmeters are introduced.

Chapter 3. Resistance: Resistance terminology and applications are introduced including resistance, conductance, characteristic curves, shorts, opens, diodes, resistor color code, and resistance measurements. Characteristic curves are used throughout the text to represent devices like diodes and MOSFETs when appropriate. Ohm's law is introduced as a static resistance point on a characteristic curve. The use of Ohm's law for circuit analysis is deferred until after a thorough understanding of Kirchhoff's laws and their applications are developed in Chapters 5 and 6.

Chapter 4. Resistance Applications: Resistance applications of wire, fuses and circuit breakers, potentiometers and rheostats, temperature effects, and sensors are introduced. Shorts and opens are introduced as a modeling tool for devices.

Chapter 5. KCL—Kirchhoff's Current Law: This basic circuit law is established and applied to several passive and electronic circuits including a BJT amplifier and an op amp inverting summing circuit.

Chapter 6. KVL—Kirchhoff's Voltage Law: This basic circuit law is firmly established in terms of voltage drops, node voltages, and closed or open voltage loops. Special focus is provided on differentiating and applying voltage drops and node voltages to passive and electronic circuits including BJT, MOSFET, and op amp devices.

Chapter 7. Ohm's Law, Power, and Energy: After the foundational circuit laws of KCL and KVL have been firmly rooted in circuit analysis, Ohm's law of resistance is introduced for the purpose of circuit analysis. The power rule and the resistive form of the power rule are introduced and applied to devices and circuits. Applications include BJT, MOSFET, and op amp circuits. Energy and the cost of energy are examined.

Chapter 8. Series Circuits: Series circuit characteristics are developed from foundational circuit laws and applied to passive and active circuits. The Thévenin model is introduced as a simple series circuit from a "What's in the box?" modeling approach.

Chapter 9. Essentially Series Circuits: Much of electronic circuit analysis reduces down to an essentially series circuit analysis when realistic, simplifying assumptions are made. The ideal op amp and its physical limitations are introduced and then utilized in comparator, positive feedback comparator, and negative feedback amplifier circuits. Electronic application circuits such as inverting and noninverting comparators with and without positive feedback, inverting and noninverting voltage amplifiers including the buffer amplifier, composite amplifiers with active devices in the negative feedback loop, and active diode circuits serve as applications of this simple principle of essentially series circuits.

Note: Chapter 9 can be effectively deferred until after Chapter 11, thus producing the sequence of Chapter 8—Series Circuits, Chapter 10—Parallel Circuits, Chapter 11—Series-Parallel Circuits, and Chapter 9—Essentially Series Circuits.

Chapter 10. Parallel Circuits: Parallel circuit characteristics are developed from foundational circuit laws and applied to passive and active circuits. The Norton model is introduced as a simple parallel circuit from a "What's in the box?" modeling approach.

Chapter 11. Series-Parallel Circuits: Series-parallel circuit characteristics are developed from foundational circuit laws and applied to passive and active circuits. Resistive reduction techniques and basic circuit analysis techniques are used to analyze passive and electronic circuits such as the active R-2R ladder network (fundamental building block of a DAC).

Chapter 12. Waveforms: Basic alternating waveform terminology, ac supplies, ac with offset supplies, average power (rms), and superposition of signals are introduced and applied to passive and electronic circuits. Measurement of ac and ac with dc offset is included.

Chapter 13. Capacitance and Reactance: This chapter introduces capacitance and the capacitor, capacitive reactance, series and parallel combinations of capacitance, and the use of the capacitor as a coupling and filter capacitor in passive and active circuits. The technique of the quick-look effect of a capacitor as a short to ac and an open to dc (or very low frequency ac) is applied to electronic circuits.

Chapter 14. *RC* Switching Circuits: *RC* transient switching circuits are analyzed by determining and utilizing the initial, steady state, and charging time constant values. These three key values determine the dc universal *RC* transient response equations and curves and form the basis for *RC* timing circuit applications. This chapter includes the *RC* square wave response curves and associated time constant, rise time, and fall time values of a signal response.

Chapter 15. Wave Shaping and Generation: This chapter covers signal generating and waveshaping circuits. Topics include *RC* multivibrators, integrators, differentiators, hidden capacitance, clippers, clampers, detectors, and switched capacitor circuits.

Chapter 16. Inductance and *RL* Circuits: This chapter introduces inductance and the inductor, inductor reactance, series and parallel combinations of inductance, the *RL* dc transient response, *RL* square wave response, *RLC* effects and compensation, and *RL* application circuits.

Chapter 17. Transformers: The ideal transformer and its voltage, current, and power relationships are examined and applied. The transformer secondary is also viewed and analyzed as an ac Thévenin source.

Chapter 18. Power Supply Applications: The dc power supply is described and analyzed including the transformer action, rectifier circuits, light and heavy discharge filtering, light and heavy load regulation, and heat sinking. The principles of the previous chapters are pulled together to build and systematically analyze the power supply circuit.

Chapter 19. Dependent Sources: Active circuits are modeled as dependent sources, a technique used to analyze op amp, MOSFET, and BJT application circuits. Maximum signal transfer and appropriate model types are described and applied.

Chapter 20. Special Analog Integrated Circuits: The Exar 2206 and the Lattice ispPAC 10 are specialized analog integrated circuits (ICs). The ispPAC 10 is a programmable analog device that can be programmed to imitate different analog devices. The Exar 2206 is an IC function generator which can generate sine, square, and triangle wave shapes.

Instructor's Guide

Chapter 1

1-1   Foot; meter; centimeter; meter

1-2   Fahrenheit; Centigrade; Kelvin; Centigrade

1-3 $\dfrac{14.8\ \text{m} - 15\ \text{m}}{15\ \text{m}} = -1.33\%$

1-4   2%

1-5   **a.** 1, **b.** 3, **c.** 1, **d.** 4

1-6   **a.** 1, **b.** 4, **c.** 1, **d.** 2

1-7   Nearest millimeter

1-8   Nearest degree

1-9 $10.5\ \text{m} \leq X < 11.5\ \text{m}$

1-10 $24.5°\text{C} \leq t < 25.5°\text{C}$

1-11   20 (unit place)

1-12   2 (unit place)

1-13   1000 (1 significant figure)

1-14   30 (1 significant figure)

1-15   **a.** 10^0, **b.** 10^2, **c.** 10^4, **d.** 10^{-1}, **e.** 10^{-3}, **f.** 10^{-5}

1-16   **a.** 10^1, **b.** 10^3, **c.** 10^5, **d.** 10^{-2}, **e.** 10^{-4}, **f.** 10^{-10}

1-17   **a.** 5×10^1, **b.** 12×10^4, **c.** 43×10^{-3}, **d.** 7×10^{-5}

1-18   **a.** 43×10^1, **b.** 8×10^4, **c.** 93×10^{-2}, **d.** 101×10^{-6}

1-19   **a.** 10^5, **b.** 10^1, **c.** 10^3, **d.** 10^6, **e.** 10^6, **f.** 10^{-6}, **g.** -10^4, **h.** 10^{-4}

1-20   **a.** 10^7, **b.** 10^{-3}, **c.** 10^1, **d.** 10^2, **e.** 10^6, **f.** 10^{-6}, **g.** -10^{-4}, **h.** 10^6

1-21   **a.** 6×10^2, **b.** 33×10^2, **c.** 8×10^6, **d.** 12×10^4, **e.** 6×10^3, **f.** 6×10^6, **g.** 16×10^6, **h.** 8×10^{-6}

1-22   **a.** 6×10^{-2}, **b.** 33×10^{-3}, **c.** 8×10^2, **d.** 12×10^{-6}, **e.** 6×10^{-7}, **f.** 6×10^{-6}, **g.** 625×10^{-10}, **h.** 125×10^3

1-23   **a.** 128, **b**. -72×10^7

1-24   **a.** 16×10^{-5}, **b.** -32×10^{9}

1-25   **a.** 3.4×10^{3}, **b.** 5.60×10^{-3}

1-26   **a.** 3.4×10^{5}, **b.** 5.60×10^{-5}

1-27   **a.** 1.2×10^{3}, **b.** 340×10^{3}, **c.** 56.0×10^{-3}, **d.** 780×10^{-6}

1-28   **a.** 12×10^{3}, **b.** 3.4×10^{6}, **c.** 5.0×10^{-3}, **d.** 70×10^{-6}

1-29   **a.** 1.2 ks, **b.** 3.4 Ms, **c.** 56.0 ms, **d.** 780 µs

1-30   **a.** 12 ks, **b.** 340 Ms, **c.** 500 µs, **d.** 70 ns

1-31   **a.** 120 ks, **b.** 0.12 Ms, **c.** 0.00012 Gs, **d.** 0.03 ms, **e.** 30 µs, **f.** 30,000 ns

1-32   **a.** 45 ks, **b.** 0.045 Ms, **c.** 0.000045 Gs, **d.** 60 ms, **e.** 60,000 µs, **f.** 60,000,000 ns

1-33   **a.** 120 Ms, **b.** 0.12 Gs, **c.** 30 µs, **d.** 30,000 ns

1-34   **a.** 1,200 Ms, **b.** 1.2 Gs, **c.** 0.3 µs, **d.** 300 ns

1-35 $8 \text{ hr} \times \dfrac{3600 \text{ s}}{\text{hr}} \times \dfrac{10^{6} \text{ µs}}{\text{s}} \times \dfrac{3 \text{ cents}}{\text{µs}} \times \dfrac{\$1}{100 \text{ cents}} = \$\,864{,}000{,}000$

1-36 $\dfrac{\$100{,}000{,}000}{40 \text{ hr}} \times \dfrac{1 \text{ hr}}{8{,}600 \text{ s}} \times \dfrac{1 \text{ s}}{1{,}000 \text{ ms}} \times \dfrac{100 \text{ cents}}{\text{dollar}} = 69.44 \text{ cents per ms}$

1-37 $100 \text{ yd} \times \dfrac{3 \text{ ft}}{\text{yd}} \times \dfrac{12 \text{ in}}{\text{ft}} \times \dfrac{2.54 \text{ cm}}{\text{in}} = 9144 \text{ cm}$

1-38 $100 \text{ in} \times \dfrac{100 \text{ cm}}{\text{m}} \times \dfrac{1 \text{ in}}{2.54 \text{ cm}} = 3937 \text{ in}$

1-39   **a.** 120 ks, **b.** 0.12 Ms, **c.** 30 µs, **d.** 30,000 ns

1-40   **a.** 4.5 Ms, **b.** 0.0045 Gs, **c.** 60 ms, **d.** 60,000 µs

1-41   **a.** 120 Ms, **b.** 30 µs

1-42   **a.** 12 Gs, **b.** 300 ns

1-43 390.6×10^{3}

1-44 -14×10^{-3}

Chapter 2

2-1 proton: +, neutron: neutral, electron: −

2-2 repel

2-3 attract

2-4 **a.** Q, **b.** coulomb, **c.** C

2-5 **a.** 6.242×10^{18}, **b.** 6.242×10^{18}

2-6 187.3×10^{18} e

2-7 $F = \dfrac{kQ_1Q_2}{r^2}$ where $k = 9.0 \times 10^9 \, Nm^2/C^2$

2-8 $67.5 \times 10^{12} \, N$

2-9 $F = \dfrac{9.0 \times 10^9 \dfrac{Nm^2}{C^2} \times 0.1 \, C \times 0.02 \, C}{(0.05)^2 \; m^2} = \dfrac{18 \times 10^6 \; Nm^2}{2.5 \times 10^{-3} \; m^2} = 7.2 \times 10^9 \, N$

2-10 **a.** 1st shell of 2 (2), 2nd shell of 8 (2+6), 3rd shell of 3 (2+1)
b. conductor since the last subshell has only 1 electron

2-11 **a.** 1st shell of 2 (2), 2nd shell of 8 (2+6), 3rd shell of 18 (2+6+10); 4th shell of 19 (2+6+10+1)

b. conductor since the last subshell has only 1 electron

2-12 The outermost shell or band or orbiting electrons in an atom

2-13 **a.** Easily create free electrons and conduct them

b. Very hard to create free electrons and conduct them

c. Its ability to create free electrons and conduct them falls between the conductor and insulator

2-14 An outer band electron that is easily excited by external energy to leave its parent atom

2-15 An atom missing an electron

2-16 An atom with an extra electron

2-17 Yes

2-18 **a.** I, **b.** ampere or amp, **c.** A

2-19   Electron current: electrons flow from the negative supply terminal to the positive supply terminal. Conventional current: current modeled as a positive charge flowing from the positive supply terminal to its negative supply terminal.

2-20   **a.** 1 C/s, **b.** 3600 C/hour

2-21 $I = \dfrac{1800 \text{ C}}{60 \text{ s}} = 30 \text{ A}$

2-22 $I = \dfrac{240 \text{ C}}{2 \text{ min}} \times \dfrac{1 \text{ min}}{60 \text{ sec}} = 2 \text{ A}$

2-23 $I = \dfrac{15 \text{ mC}}{30 \text{ μA}} = 500 \text{ s}$

2-24   **a.** Through

2-25   Yes, to insert the ammeter

2-26   Yes, it inherently acts like a conductor

2-27   Break circuit, insert current meter with red lead toward the positive supply terminal; supply must be off to insert the meter but then turned on to measure the current

2-28   Break circuit, insert current meter with red lead toward the positive supply terminal; supply must be off to insert the meter but then turned on to measure the current

2-29   The current is actually flowing the opposite direction of the current meter connection; that is, current is flowing into the black lead instead of the red lead

2-30   **a.** $W = 150 \text{ lb} \times 300 \text{ ft} = 45,000 \text{ ft-lb} = 61.03 \text{ kJ}$, **b.** no

2-31   **a.** $W = 2000 \text{ lb} \times 300 \text{ ft} = 600,000 \text{ ft-lb} = 813.8 \text{ kJ}$, **b.** no

2-32 $P = \dfrac{61.04 \text{ kJ}}{60 \text{ s}} = 1.02 \text{ kW}$

2-33 $P = \dfrac{61.04 \text{ kJ}}{20 \text{ s}} = 3.052 \text{ kW}$

2-34   No

2-35   **a.** V (drop) or E (supply), **b.** volt, **c.** V

2-36 $W = 5 \text{ C} \times 1.5 \text{ V} = 7.5 \text{ J}$

2-37 $W = 10 \text{ C} \times 9 \text{ V} = 90 \text{ J}$

2-38 $Q = \dfrac{6 \text{ J}}{12 \text{ V}} = 0.5 \text{ C}$

2-39 $V = \dfrac{600 \text{ mJ}}{0.5 \text{ C}} = 1.2 \text{ V}$

2-40 $Q = \dfrac{100 \text{ J}}{2 \text{ V}} = 50 \text{ C}$

2-41 $V = \dfrac{100 \text{ J}}{\text{C}} = 100 \dfrac{\text{J}}{\text{C}} = 100 \text{ V}$

2-42 $W = 5 \text{ V} \times 57{,}000 \text{ C} = 285 \text{ kJ}$

2-43 Rise

2-44 Fall

2-45 Across, (**b**)

2-46 No

2-47 No (acts like an open that does not draw current)

2-48 Voltmeter put across the supply with the red lead on the positive supply terminal and black lead on the common node

2-49 Voltmeter put across the lamp with the red lead on the relatively positive terminal (top of the lamp) and black lead on the common node

2-50 Red lead on node *a* and black lead on the common node

2-51 Red lead on node *a* and black lead on node *b*.

2-52 The actual voltage polarity drop is opposite that of the voltmeter hook up, i.e., the red lead is the relatively lower voltage potential (Red lead on node *b* and black lead on node *a*)

2-53 See text

2-54 See text

2-55 See text

2-56 See text

2-57 **a.** 45 Ah, **b.** $Q = 15 \text{ A} \times 3 \text{ h} \times \dfrac{3{,}600 \text{ s}}{\text{h}} = 162 \text{ kC}$,

     c. $W = 12.6 \text{ V} \times 162 \text{ kC} = 2.041 \text{ MJ}$

2-58   **a.** 1.5 hours, **b.** $Q = 30 \text{ A} \times 1.5 \text{ h} \times \dfrac{3{,}600 \text{ s}}{\text{h}} = 162 \text{ kC}$,

   c. $t = \dfrac{162 \text{ kC}}{250 \text{ mA}} = 648 \text{ ks} \times \dfrac{1 \text{ h}}{3600 \text{ s}} = 180 \text{ hours}$

2-59   **a.** out of, **b.** clockwise, **c.** see text, **d.** positive, **e.** $V_b = 0 \text{ V}$, $V_a = 5 \text{ V}$, $V_{ab} = 5 \text{ V}$,

   f. $2 \text{ A} \times 2.5 \text{ h} = 5 \text{ Ah}$, **g.** 5 V

2-60   **a.** out of, **b.** counterclockwise, **c.** see text, **d.** negative, **e.** $V_b = 0 \text{ V}$, $V_a = -5 \text{ V}$, $V_{ab} = -5 \text{ V}$,

   f. –5 V, **g.** +5 V, **h.** $\dfrac{15 \text{ Ah}}{3 \text{ A}} = 5 \text{ hours}$

2-61   **a.** see text, **b.** $V_e = 0 \text{ V}$, $V_a = 6 \text{ V}$, $V_d = -6 \text{ V}$, **c.** red lead on node a and black lead on common,
   d. $V_{ad} = V_a - V_d = (6 \text{ V}) - (-6 \text{ V}) = 12 \text{ V}$, **e.** 4 V drops, + at top of each, **f.** $V_{ac} = 8 \text{ V}$,
   $V_{ca} = -8 \text{ V}$, **g.** red lead on node a and black lead on node c, **h.** $V_{bd} = 8 \text{ V}$, $V_{db} = -8 \text{ V}$, **i.** +6 V,
   bubble at top, –6 V bubble at bottom, no lamps connected to common

2-62   **a.** see text, **b.** $V_a = 9 \text{ V}$, $V_d = -9 \text{ V}$, **c.** $V_{ad} = V_a - V_d = 9 \text{ V} - (-9 \text{ V}) = 18 \text{ V}$, **d.** $\dfrac{V_{ad}}{3} = 6 \text{ V}$

   with + polarity at top of each lamp, **e.** $V_b = V_a - 6 \text{ V} = 3 \text{ V}$, $V_c = V_b - 6 \text{ V} = -3 \text{ V}$, **f.** red lead on
   node b and black lead on common, **g.** $V_{ac} = V_a - V_c = 9 \text{ V} - (-3 \text{ V}) = 12 \text{ V}$,

   $V_{ca} = -V_{ac} = -12 \text{ V}$, **h.** red lead on node c and black lead on node a,

   i. $V_{bd} = V_b - V_d = 3 \text{ V} - (-9 \text{ V}) = 12 \text{V}$, $V_{db} = -V_{bd} = -12 \text{ V}$, **j.** no

2-63   **a.** $V_a = 9 \text{ V}$, $V_d = 9 \text{ V}$, **b.** $V_{ad} = V_a - V_d = 9 \text{ V} - 9 \text{ V} = 0 \text{ V}$, **c.** no

Chapter 3

3-1 $R = \dfrac{4 \times 17.2 \times 10^{-9} \times 1{,}000 \text{ m}}{\pi \left(2.05 \times 10^{-3} \text{ m}\right)} = 5.211 \ \Omega$

3-2 $R = 1000 \times 10^9 \times \dfrac{3 \text{ mm}}{(4 \times 2) \text{ cm}^2} = 3.75 \text{ T}\Omega$

3-3 $G = \dfrac{1}{R} = \dfrac{1}{3.9 \text{ k}\Omega} = 256.4 \text{ μS}$

3-4 $R = \dfrac{1}{G} = \dfrac{1}{250 \text{ mS}} = 4 \text{ }\Omega$

3-5 **a.** 2 V, **b.** $R = \dfrac{V}{I} = \dfrac{4 \text{ V}}{40 \text{ mA}} = 100 \text{ }\Omega$, **c.** $G = \dfrac{1}{R} = \dfrac{1}{100 \text{ }\Omega} = 10 \text{ mS}$, **d.** 0 mA, **e.** −30 mA,

    f. $R = \dfrac{V}{I} = \dfrac{-4 \text{ V}}{-40 \text{ mA}} = 100 \text{ }\Omega$, **g.** linear, **h.** positive

3-6 **a.** 4 V, **b.** $R = \dfrac{V}{I} = \dfrac{2 \text{ V}}{20 \text{ mA}} = 100 \text{ }\Omega$, **c.** $G = \dfrac{1}{R} = \dfrac{1}{100 \text{ }\Omega} = 10 \text{ mS}$, **d.** −20 mA,

    e. $R = \dfrac{V}{I} = \dfrac{2 \text{ V}}{20 \text{ mA}} = 200 \text{ }\Omega$, **f.** nonlinear

3-7 **b.** 0 V

3-8 **a.** 0 A

3-9 SW 1 down, SW 3 closed

3-10 SW 1 up, SW 2 closed

3-11 **a.** reverse, **b.** off, **c.** no

3-12 **a.** forward, **b.** on, **c.** yes

3-13 **a.** $270 \text{ k}\Omega \pm 5\%$, $R_{max} = 270 \text{ k}\Omega + 0.05(270 \text{ k}\Omega) = 283.5 \text{ k}\Omega$,
    $R_{min} = 270 \text{ k}\Omega - 0.05(270 \text{ k}\Omega) = 256.5 \text{ k}\Omega$,
    b. $1.8 \text{ k}\Omega \pm 10\%$, $R_{max} = 1.8 \text{ k}\Omega + 0.10(1.8 \text{ k}\Omega) = 1.98 \text{ k}\Omega$,
    $R_{min} = 1.8 \text{ k}\Omega - 0.10(1.8 \text{ k}\Omega) = 1.62 \text{ k}\Omega$,
    c. $10 \text{ }\Omega \pm 20\%$, $R_{max} = 10 \text{ }\Omega + 0.20(10 \text{ }\Omega) = 12 \text{ }\Omega$, $R_{min} = 10 \text{ }\Omega - 0.20(10 \text{ }\Omega) = 8 \text{ }\Omega$

3-14 **a.** $1 \text{ M}\Omega \pm 5\%$, $R_{max} = 1 \text{ M}\Omega + 0.05(1 \text{ M}\Omega) = 1.05 \text{ M}\Omega$,
    $R_{min} = 1 \text{ M}\Omega - 0.05(1 \text{ M}\Omega) = 0.95 \text{ M}\Omega$, **b.** $39 \text{ k}\Omega \pm 10\%$,
    $R_{max} = 39 \text{ k}\Omega + 0.10(39 \text{ k}\Omega) = 42.9 \text{ k}\Omega$, $R_{min} = 39 \text{ k}\Omega - 0.10(39 \text{ k}\Omega) = 35.1 \text{ k}\Omega$,
    c. $560 \text{ }\Omega \pm 20\%$, $R_{max} = 560 \text{ }\Omega + 0.20(560 \text{ }\Omega) = 672 \text{ }\Omega$,
    $R_{min} = 460 \text{ }\Omega - 0.20(560 \text{ }\Omega) = 448 \text{ }\Omega$

3-15 No

3-16 No. The ohmmeter has its own internal supply to create a current through and a voltage across the test resistance, then calculates $R = V/I$.

3-17 $R = \dfrac{V}{I} = \dfrac{1.5 \text{ V}}{15 \text{ mA}} = 100 \text{ } \Omega$

3-18 Maybe. The diode needs enough forward bias voltage to turn it on (Ge, 0.2 V; Si, 0.7 V)

Chapter 4

4-1 $A_{14} = 2.08 \text{ mm}^2$; $A_{24} = 0.205 \text{ mm}^2$, $\dfrac{A_{14}}{A_{24}} = \dfrac{2.08 \text{ mm}^2}{.205 \text{ mm}^2} = 10.15$

4-2 $R_{14} = 210 \dfrac{\mu\Omega}{\text{in}} \times \dfrac{12 \text{ in}}{\text{ft}} \times \dfrac{300 \text{ ft}}{1} = 0.756 \text{ } \Omega$; $R_{24} = 2139 \dfrac{\mu\Omega}{\text{in}} \times \dfrac{12 \text{ in}}{\text{ft}} \times \dfrac{300 \text{ ft}}{1} = 7.70 \text{ } \Omega$;

$\dfrac{R_{24}}{R_{14}} = \dfrac{7.70 \text{ } \Omega}{0.756 \text{ } \Omega} = 10.19$

4-3 AWG 10

4-4 A blown open fuse must be replaced; a tripped breaker just reset.

4-5 Slow blow allows for current spikes and must remain above rated current capacity for a few seconds.

4-6 a short

4-7 15 kΩ

4-8 **a.** 50 kΩ, 20 kΩ, 30 kΩ, **b.** 20 kΩ and 30 kΩ fixed resistances

4-9 Wiper arm shorted to unused wiper arm to prevent unused terminal from acting like an antenna

4-10 **a.** positive, **b.** negative, **c.** negative

4-11 $m = 0.0045 \text{ °C}^{-1} \times 20 \text{ } \Omega = 0.090 \dfrac{\Omega}{\text{°C}}$,

$R_2 = 20 \text{ } \Omega + 0.090 \dfrac{\Omega}{\text{°C}} (2{,}820 \text{ °C} - 20 \text{ °C}) = 20 \text{ } \Omega + 252 \text{ } \Omega = 272 \text{ } \Omega$

Chapter 5

5-1 $I_x = 12 \text{ A} - 3 \text{ A} = 9 \text{ A}$

5-2 $I_x = 0 \text{ A} - 9 \text{ A} = -9 \text{ A}$

5-3 **a.** $I_1 = I_6 = 20 \text{ mA}$, $I_2 = I_5 = 4 \text{ mA} + 7 \text{ mA} = 11 \text{ mA}$,
$I_3 = I_1 - I_2 = 20 \text{ mA} - 11 \text{ mA} = 9 \text{ mA}$, $I_4 = 4 \text{ mA}$, **b.** circle cuts only I_2 & I_5,
c. circle cuts only I_1 & I_6

5-4 **a.** $I_1 = 1 \text{ mA} + 2 \text{ mA} = 3 \text{ mA}$, $I_2 = I_1 = 3 \text{ mA}$, $I_3 = I_4 = 4 \text{ mA} + 3 \text{ mA} = 7 \text{ mA}$,
$I_{\text{supply}} = I_1 + I_3 = I_2 + I_4 = 10 \text{ mA}$, **b.** circle cuts only I_1 & I_2, **c.** circle cuts only I_3 & I_4

5-5 **a.** $I_x = 1 \text{ A} + 1 \text{ A} = 2 \text{ A}$, $I_{\text{lamp}} = I_x + 1 \text{ A} = 2 \text{ A} + 1 \text{ A} = 3 \text{ A}$,

b. $I_{\text{lamp}} = I_{V1} + I_{V2} + I_{V3} = 1 \text{ A} + 1 \text{ A} + 1 \text{ A} = 3 \text{ A}$,

c. $I_{\text{lamp}} = I_{V1} + I_{V2} + I_{V3} = 1 \text{ A} + 1 \text{ A} + 1 \text{ A} = 3 \text{ A}$

5-6 **a.** $I_{\text{supply}} = 2(8 \text{ A}) + 2(4 \text{ A}) = 24 \text{ A}$, **b.** 25 A fuse, **c.** —, **d.** 0 A

5-7 **a.** $I_B = \dfrac{I_C}{\beta} = \dfrac{10 \text{ mA}}{200} = 50 \text{ μA}$, **b.** $I_E = I_B + I_C = 10 \text{ mA} + 50 \text{ μA} = 10.05 \text{ mA}$,

c. $I_{\text{LED}} = I_E = 10.05 \text{ mA}$, **d.** $I_C = I_E = 0 \text{ ma}$, no

5-8 **a.** $I_{\text{in}} = 40 \text{ μA} + I_{R2} + 10 \text{ μA} + (-30 \text{ μA}) = 0 \text{ A}$, $20 \text{ μA} + I_{R2} = 0 \text{ A}$, $I_{R2} = -20 \text{ μA}$,

b. out of, **c.** $I_{\text{out op amp}} = -30 \text{ μA} + 40 \text{ μA} = 10 \text{ μA}$

5-9 **a.** $I_{Rf} = I_{Ri} = 5 \text{ mA}$, **b.** $I_{\text{out op amp}} = I_{Rf} + I_{\text{load}} = 5 \text{ mA} + 10 \text{ mA} = 15 \text{ mA}$

Chapter 6

6-1 **a.** $\sum V_{rise} - \sum V_{falls} = 0 \text{ V}$, $18 \text{ V} - 4 \text{ V} - 12 \text{ V} - V_{R2} = 0 \text{ V}$, $V_{R2} = 2 \text{ V}$, **b.** 2 V, **c.** $V_a = 18 \text{ V}$,
$V_b = 18 \text{ V} - 4 \text{ V} = 14 \text{ V}$, $V_c = 12 \text{ V}$, **d.** $V_{bc} = V_b - V_c = 14 \text{ V} - 12 \text{ V} = 2 \text{ V}$

6-2 **a.** $V_{R2} = 16 \text{ V} - 12 \text{ V} = 4 \text{ V}$, **b.** $V_L = 4 \text{ V} - 3 \text{ V} = 1 \text{ V}$, **c.** $V_{R3} = 1 \text{ V} + 12 \text{ V} = 13 \text{ V}$,

d. $V_2 = -3 \text{ V} + 16 \text{ V} - 12 \text{ V} = 1 \text{ V}$

6-3   **a.** $V_a = +12\ \text{V} - 9\ \text{V} = 3\ \text{V}$, **b.** 2 V, **c.** $V_{ab} = V_a - V_b = 3\ \text{V} - 2\ \text{V} = 1\ \text{V}$,

   d. $-2\ \text{V} + 12\ \text{V} - 9\ \text{V} = V_{ab} = 1\ \text{V}$

6-4   **a.** —, **b.** 2 V, **c.** $V_b = V_e + 0.7\ \text{V} = 2.7\ \text{V}$, **d.** 7 V, **e.** $V_{RB} = 7\ \text{V} - 2.7\ \text{V} = 4.3\ \text{V}$,

   f. $-0.7\ \text{V} - 2\ \text{V} + 7\ \text{V} = V_{RB} = 4.3\ \text{V}$, **g.** $V_C = 15\ \text{V} - 3\ \text{V} = 12\ \text{V}$,

   h. $V_{CE} = V_C - V_E = 12\ \text{V} - 2\ \text{V} = 10\ \text{V}$

6-5 $E_{in} = V_{gs} + V_{load} = 4.4\ \text{V} + 9.6\ \text{V} = 14\ \text{V}$, $V_{DS} = 12\ \text{V} - 9.6\ \text{V} = 2.4\ \text{V}$,

   $R_{DS} = \dfrac{2.4\ \text{V}}{3.2\ \text{A}} = \dfrac{3\ \text{V}}{4\ \text{A}} = 0.75\ \Omega$ or 750 mΩ

6-6   **a.** 0 V, **b.** $V_{Ri} = 1\ \text{V} - 0\ \text{V} = 1\ \text{V}$, **c.** $V_{out} = V_a - V_{Rf} = 0\ \text{V} - 5\ \text{V} = -5\ \text{V}$

Chapter 7

7-1 $I = \dfrac{12\ \text{V}}{2.2\ \text{k}\Omega} = 5.455\ \text{mA}$

7-2 $V = 3\ \text{mA} \times 1.8\ \text{k}\Omega = 5.4\ \text{V}$

7-3 $R = \dfrac{18\ \text{V}}{10\ \text{mA}} = 1.8\ \text{k}\Omega$

7-4   **a.** yes, **b.** —, **c.** 9 V, $I = \dfrac{9\ \text{V}}{220\ \Omega} = 40.9\ \text{mA}$, **d.** —, **e.** line from (15 V, 68.2 mA) through origin to (–15 V, –68.2 mA)

7-5   **a.** See text, **b.** –6 V, $I_R = \dfrac{-6\ \text{V}}{1.2\ \text{k}\Omega} = -5\ \text{mA}$, **c.** See text, **d.** line from (10 V, 8.33 mA) through origin to (–10 V, –8.33 mA)

7-6 $P = 12\ \text{V} \times 3\ \text{A} = 36\ \text{W}$

7-7 $I = \dfrac{46\ \text{mW}}{2.3\ \text{V}} = 20\ \text{mA}$

7-8 $\quad V = \dfrac{10\ \text{W}}{0.5\ \text{A}} = 20\ \text{V}$

7-9 $\quad P = (200\ \text{mA})^2 \times 100\ \Omega = 4\ \text{W},\ \ \text{unsafe}$

7-10 $\quad P = \dfrac{10\ \text{V}^2}{3.3\ \text{k}\Omega} = 30.3\ \text{mW, safe}$

7-11 $\quad I = \sqrt{\dfrac{10\ \text{W}}{1\ \text{k}\Omega}} = 100\ \text{mA},\ V = \sqrt{10\ \text{W} \times 1\ \text{k}\Omega} = 100\ \text{V},$

7-12 $\quad I = \sqrt{\dfrac{2\ \text{W}}{39\ \Omega}} = 226\ \text{mW},\ V = \sqrt{2\ \text{W} \times 39\ \Omega} = 8.83\ \text{V}$

7-13 $\quad I = \sqrt{\dfrac{0.25\ \text{W}}{180\ \Omega}} = 37.3\ \text{mA}$

7-14 $\quad V = \sqrt{0.50\ \text{W} \times 180\ \Omega} = 6.71\ \text{V}$

7-15 **a.** $V_{\text{RB}} = 6\ \text{V} - 0.7\ \text{V} = 5.3\ \text{V}$, **b.** $I_{\text{RB}} = \dfrac{5.3\ \text{V}}{100\ \text{k}\Omega} = 53\ \mu\text{A}$, **c.** $P_{\text{BE}} = 53\ \mu\text{A} \times 0.7\ \text{V} = 37\ \mu\text{W}$,

   d. $V_{\text{CE}} = 20\ \text{V} - 2\ \text{V} - 2\ \text{V} = 16\ \text{V}$, **e.** $P_{\text{CE}} = 10\ \text{mA} \times 16\ \text{V} = 160\ \text{mW}$, **f.** $\beta = \dfrac{10\ \text{mA}}{53\ \mu\text{A}} = 189$

7-16 **a.** $V_{\text{load}} = +18\ \text{V} - 2\ \text{V} - 10\ \text{V} = 6\ \text{V}$, **b.** $I_{\text{load}} = \dfrac{6\ \text{V}}{2\ \Omega} 3\ \text{A}$, **c.** 4.4 V, **d.** $E_{\text{in}} = 4.4\ \text{V} + 6\ \text{V} = 10.4\ \text{V}$

   e. $P_{\text{load}} = 6\ \text{V} \times 3\ \text{A} = 18\ \text{W}$, **f.** $P_{\text{Q}} = 10\ \text{V} \times 3\ \text{A} = 30\ \text{W}$, **g.** $P_{\text{lamp}} = 2\ \text{V} \times 3\ \text{A} = 6\ \text{W}$,

   h. $P_{\text{supply}} = 18\ \text{V} \times 3\ \text{A} = 54\ \text{W}$, **i.** $54\ \text{W} = 18\ \text{W} + 30\ \text{W} + 6\ \text{W}$

7-17 **a.** 0 V, **b.** 1 V, **c.** $I_{\text{Ri}} = I_{\text{Rf}} = \dfrac{1\ \text{V}}{1\ \text{k}\Omega} = 1\ \text{mA}$, **d.** $I_{\text{Ri}} = I_{\text{Rf}} = \dfrac{1\ \text{V}}{1\ \text{k}\Omega} = 1\ \text{mA}$,

   e. $V_{\text{Rf}} = 1\ \text{mA} \times 2.7\ \text{k}\Omega = 2.7\ \text{V}$, **f.** $V_{\text{out}} = V_{\text{load}} = 0\ \text{V} - 2.7\ \text{V} = -2.7\ \text{V}$,

   g. $V_{\text{out}} = V_{\text{load}} = 0\ \text{V} - 2.7\ \text{V} = -2.7\ \text{V}$, **h.** $I_{\text{load}} = \dfrac{-2.7\ \text{V}}{10\ \text{k}\Omega} = -0.27\ \text{mA}$,

i. $I_{\text{op amp}} = 1 \text{ mA} - 270 \text{ μA} = 1.27 \text{ mA}$ into op amp

7-18 $W = 0.1 \text{ kW} \times \left(1 \text{ yr} \times \dfrac{365 \text{ days}}{\text{yr}} \times \dfrac{24 \text{ hrs}}{\text{day}}\right) = 876 \text{ kWh}, \text{ cost} = \dfrac{9 \text{ cents}}{\text{kWh}} \times 876 \text{ kWh} = 7884 \text{ cents}$ or

$78.84

7-19 $P = 12 \text{ V} \times 200 \text{ mA} = 2.4 \text{ W}, \text{ cost} = 2.4 \text{ W} \times 125 \text{ days} \times \dfrac{24 \text{ hrs}}{\text{day}} = 7.2 \text{ kWh} \times \dfrac{10 \text{ cts}}{\text{kWh}} = 72 \text{ cents}$

7-20   out of positive terminal, sourcing current

7-21   into positive terminal, sinking current

Chapter 8

8-1   **a.** See Figure 8-40, **b.** $V_R = 15 \text{ V} - 2 \text{ V} = 13 \text{ V}$, **c.** $I_{\text{LED}} = \dfrac{13 \text{ V}}{1 \text{ kΩ}} = 13 \text{ mA}$

8-2   **a.** See Figure 8-40, **b.** $V_R = -15 \text{ V} - (-2 \text{ V}) = -13 \text{ V}$, **c.** $I_{\text{LED}} = \dfrac{-13 \text{ V}}{1 \text{ kΩ}} = -13 \text{ mA}$

8-3   **a.** $E = I*(R_1 + R_2 + R_3)$, **b.** $I = \dfrac{11 \text{ V}}{1.1 \text{ kΩ}} = 10 \text{ mA}$, **c.** $V_{R1} = 10 \text{ mA} \times 150 \text{ Ω} = 1.5 \text{ V}$,

$V_{R2} = 10 \text{ mA} \times 270 \text{ Ω} = 2.7 \text{ V}$, $V_{R3} = 10 \text{ mA} \times 680 \text{ Ω} = 6.8 \text{ V}$

d. $V_a = 11 \text{ V}$, $V_b = 2.7 \text{ V} + 6.8 \text{ V} = 9.5 \text{ V}$, $V_c = 9.5 \text{ V} - 2.7 \text{ V} = 6.8 \text{ V}$, $V_d = 0 \text{ V}$,

e. $V_{ac} = 11 \text{ V} - 6.8 \text{ V} = 4.2 \text{ V}$, $V_{ca} = 6.8 \text{ V} - 11 \text{ V} = -4.2 \text{ V}$, **f.** $R_T = \dfrac{11 \text{ V}}{10 \text{ mA}} = 1.1 \text{ kΩ}$,

g. —

8-4   **a.** $R_T = 1 \text{ kΩ} + 2.7 \text{ kΩ} + 3.3 \text{ kΩ} = 7 \text{ kΩ}$, **b.** 7 V, –7 V, **c.** $V_{ad} = 7 \text{ V} - (-7 \text{ V}) = 14 \text{ V}$,

d. $I = \dfrac{14 \text{ V}}{7 \text{ kΩ}} = 2 \text{ mA}$, **e.** $V_{R1} = 14 \text{ V} \times \dfrac{1 \text{ kΩ}}{7 \text{ kΩ}} = 2 \text{ V}$, $V_{R2} = 14 \text{ V} \times \dfrac{2.7 \text{ kΩ}}{7 \text{ kΩ}} = 5.4 \text{ V}$,

$V_{R3} = 14 \text{ V} \times \dfrac{3.3 \text{ kΩ}}{7 \text{ kΩ}} = 6.6 \text{ V}$, **f.** $V_b = 7 \text{ V} - 2 \text{ V} = 5 \text{ V}$, $V_c = 5 \text{ V} - 5.5 \text{ V} = -0.4 \text{ V}$,

g. $V_{ac} = 7 \text{ V} - (-0.4 \text{ V}) = 7.4 \text{ V}$, $V_{bd} = 5 \text{ V} - (-7 \text{ V}) = 12 \text{ V}$, –12 V, **h.**—

8-5   **a.** $R_T = 150\ \Omega + 270\ \Omega + 680\ \Omega = 1.1\ \text{k}\Omega$, **b.** $I_T = \dfrac{11\ \text{V}}{1.1\ \text{k}\Omega} = 10\ \text{mA}$

8-6   **a.** $R_T = 1\ \text{k}\Omega + 2.7\ \text{k}\Omega + 3.3\ \text{k}\Omega = 7\ \text{k}\Omega$, **b.** $I = \dfrac{14\ \text{V}}{7\ \text{k}\Omega} = 2\ \text{mA}$

8-7   **a.** $R_T = \dfrac{13\ \text{V}}{20\ \text{mA}} = 650\ \Omega$, **b.** $R_1 = 650\ \Omega - 220\ \Omega - 330\ \Omega = 100\ \Omega$,

   c. $P_T = 13\ \text{V} \times 20\ \text{mA} = 260\ \text{mW}$, **d.** $P_{R3} = (20\ \text{mA})^2 \times 330\ \Omega = 132\ \text{mW}$, yes

8-8   **a.** $V_{R2} = 20\ \text{mA} \times 220\ \Omega = 4.4\ \text{V}$, $V_{R3} = 20\ \text{mA} \times 330\ \Omega = 6.6\ \text{V}$,

   b. $V_{R1} = 13\ \text{V} - 4.4\ \text{V} - 6.6\ \text{V} = 2\ \text{V}$, **c.** $R_1 = \dfrac{2\ \text{V}}{20\ \text{mA}} = 100\ \Omega$, yes

8-9   **a.** $I = \dfrac{10\ \text{V}}{10\ \Omega + 10\ \Omega} = 500\ \text{mA}$, **b.** $I = \dfrac{10\ \text{V}}{10\ \Omega + 10\ \Omega + 1\ \Omega} = 476\ \text{mA}$,

   c. $\% \ error = \dfrac{476.2\ \text{mA} - 500\ \text{mA}}{500\ \text{mA}} \times 100\ \% = -4.76\ \%$, yes

8-10 $I = \dfrac{10\ \text{V}}{10\ \Omega}\ 1\ \text{A}$, $I_{R1} = 1\ \text{A}$, $I_{R2} = 0\ \text{A}$, the meter, power supply, and R1

8-11   **a.** $V_{R1} = 11\ \text{V} \times \dfrac{150\ \Omega}{1.1\ \text{k}\Omega} = 1.5\ \text{V}$, $V_{R2} = 11\ \text{V} \times \dfrac{270\ \Omega}{1.1\ \text{k}\Omega} = 2.7\ \text{V}$, $V_{R3} = 11\ \text{V} \times \dfrac{680\ \Omega}{1.1\ \text{k}\Omega} = 6.8\ \text{V}$,

   b. $V_{ac} = 11\ \text{V} \times \dfrac{420\ \Omega}{1.1\ \text{k}\Omega} = 4.2\ \text{V}$, **c.** $V_{bd} = 11\ \text{V} \times \dfrac{950\ \Omega}{1.1\ \text{k}\Omega} = 9.5\ \text{V}$,

   d. $V_{db} = -11\ \text{V} \times \dfrac{950\ \Omega}{1.1\ \text{k}\Omega} = -9.5\ \text{V}$

8-12   **a.** $V_{R1} = 14\ \text{V} \times \dfrac{1\ \text{k}\Omega}{7\ \text{k}\Omega} = 2\ \text{V}$, $V_{R2} = 14\ \text{V} \times \dfrac{2.7\ \text{k}\Omega}{7\ \text{k}\Omega} = 5.4\ \text{V}$, $V_{R3} = 14\ \text{V} \times \dfrac{3.3\ \text{k}\Omega}{7\ \text{k}\Omega} = 6.6\ \text{V}$,

   b. $V_{ac} = 14\ \text{V} \times \dfrac{1\ \text{k}\Omega + 2.7\ \text{k}\Omega}{7\ \text{k}\Omega} = 7.4\ \text{V}$, **c.** $V_{bd} = 14\ \text{V} \times \dfrac{2.7\ \text{k}\Omega + 3.3\ \text{k}\Omega}{7\ \text{k}\Omega} = 12\ \text{V}$,

d. −12 V

8-13   **a.** $V_B = +18 \text{ V} \times \dfrac{2.2 \text{ k}\Omega}{9 \text{ k}\Omega} = 4.4 \text{ V}$,   **b.** $V_E = 4.4 \text{ V} - 0.7 \text{ V} = 3.7 \text{ V}$,   **c.** $I_E = \dfrac{3.7 \text{ V}}{1 \text{ k}\Omega} = 3.7 \text{ mA}$,

   d. $I_C = 3.7 \text{ mA}$ **e.** $V_C = +18 \text{ V} - 2 \text{ V} = 16 \text{ V}$,   **f.** $V_{CE} = 16 \text{ V} - 3.7 \text{ V} = 12.3 \text{ V}$

   g. $I_B = \dfrac{3.7 \text{ mA}}{250} = 15 \text{ μA}$,   **h.** yes, $I_{R1} = \dfrac{18 \text{ V} - 4.4 \text{ V}}{1.8 \text{ K}\Omega} = 2 \text{ mA} \gg 15 \text{ μA}$

8-14   **a.** $I_B = \dfrac{3.7 \text{ mA}}{10} = 0.37 \text{ mA}$,   **b.** no, $I_{R1} = \dfrac{18 \text{ V} - 4.4 \text{ V}}{1.8 \text{ k}\Omega} = 2 \text{ mA not} \gg 0.37 \text{ mA}$

8-15 $R_1 = \dfrac{(18 \text{ V} \times 2.2 \text{ k}\Omega) - (5.9 \text{ V} \times 2.2 \text{ k}\Omega)}{5.9 \text{ V}} = \dfrac{26.62 \text{ k}\Omega \text{ V}}{5.9 \text{ V}} = 4.5 \text{ k}\Omega$

8-16   **a.** 4.4 V,   **b.** 3 mA,   **c.** 12 V,   **d.** 36 W

8-17 $R_2 = \dfrac{4.2 \text{ V} \times 68 \text{ k}\Omega}{18 \text{ V} - 4.2 \text{ V}} = \dfrac{285.6 \text{ k}\Omega \text{ V}}{13.8 \text{ V}} = 20.7 \text{ k}\Omega$

8-18   **a.** 18 V,   **b.** 17.9 Ω,   **c.** 0.1 V,   **d.** 0.1 Ω,   **e.** 17.9 W,   **f.** −0.56 %,   **g.** 180 A (theoretically), definitely a problem

8-19   **a.** 1.6 V,   **b.** $R_L = \dfrac{1.45 \text{ V}}{1 \text{ A}} = 1.45 \text{ Ω}$,   **c.** $V_{R \text{ supply}} = 1.6 \text{ V} - 1.45 \text{ V} = 0.15 \text{ V}$,

   d. $R_{\text{supply}} = \dfrac{0.15 \text{ V}}{1 \text{ A}} = 0.15 \text{ Ω}$,   **e.** $\% VR = \dfrac{1.6 \text{ V} - 1.45 \text{ V}}{1.45 \text{ V}} \times 100 \% = -10.34 \%$

8-20   **a.** 12 V,   **b.** 4 kΩ,   **c.** 12 V series with 4 kΩ   **d.** 4 V, 2 mA

8-21   **a.** 20 V,   **b.** $R_{TH} = \dfrac{20 \text{ V} - 5 \text{ V}}{5 \text{ mA}} = \dfrac{15 \text{ V}}{5 \text{ mA}} = 3 \text{ kΩ}$,   **c.** 20 V series with 3 kΩ,

   d. $V_L = 20 \text{ V} \times \dfrac{2 \text{ k}\Omega}{5 \text{ k}\Omega} = 8 \text{ V}$, $I_L = \dfrac{8 \text{ V}}{2 \text{ k}\Omega} = 4 \text{ mA}$

8-22   **a.** See text,   **b.** 6 V,   **c.** 2.5 A,   **d.** 2.4 Ω

8-23   **a.** See text,   **b.** $E_{\text{Total}} = 1.5 \text{ V} + 1.5 \text{ V} + 1.5 \text{ V} - 1.5 \text{ V} = 3 \text{ V}$

8-24   **a.** 9 V, 0.9 A; 0 V,   **b.** 8.3 V, 0.83 A; 0.7 V,   **c.** 8.0 V, 0.8 A, 1.02 V

8-25   **a.** $V_R = 9\text{ V} - 5\text{ V} = 4\text{ V}, \quad I_P = \dfrac{4\text{ V}}{120\ \Omega} = 33.3\text{ mA; 5 V,}$

      b. $V_R = (9\text{ V} - 5\text{ V}) \times \dfrac{120\ \Omega}{128\ \Omega} = 3.75\text{ V}, \quad I_D = \dfrac{3.75\text{ V}}{120\ \Omega} = 31.25\text{ mA,}$

      $V_{out} = 5\text{ V} + (31.25\text{ mA} \times 8\ \Omega) = 5.25\text{ V}$

Chapter 9

9-1   **a.** $V_{error} = 7\ \mu V - 2\ \mu V = 5\ \mu V,$ **b.** $V_{error} = 5\ \mu V - (-2)\ \mu V = 7\ \mu V,$

      c. $V_{error} = 7\ \mu V - 0\text{ V} = 7\ \mu V,$ **d.** $V_{error} = 0\text{ V} - 7\ \mu V = -7\ \mu V$

9-2   **a.** $V_{error} = 2\ \mu V - 7\ \mu V = -5\ \mu V,$ **b.** $V_{error} = -1\ \mu V - 7\ \mu V = -8\ \mu V,$

      c. $V_{error} = -7\ \mu V - 0\text{ V} = -7\ \mu V,$ **d.** $V_{error} = 0\text{ V} - (-7)\ \mu V = 7\ \mu V$

9-3   **a.** safe, **b.** safe, **c.** unsafe, **d.** unsafe

9-4   **a.** safe, **b.** unsafe, **c.** safe, **d.** unsafe

9-5   **a.** $V_{out\ op\ amp} = 10^5 \times (5\ \mu V - 7\ \mu V) = -200\text{ mV,}$ **b.** $V_{out\ op\ amp} = 10^5 \times (2\ \mu V - 5\ \mu V) = 700\text{ mV,}$

      c. $V_{out\ op\ amp} = 10^5 \times (2\text{ V} - 0\text{ V}) = 200\text{ kV} \rangle 13\text{ V} = 13\text{ V}$

9-6   **a.** $V_{out\ op\ amp} = 10^5 \times (-1\ \mu V - 4\ \mu V) = -500\text{ mV}$

      b. $V_{out\ op\ amp} = 10^5 \times (-1\ \mu V - (-4)\ \mu V) = 300\text{ mV}$

      c. $V_{out\ op\ amp} = 10^5 \times (-2\ \mu V - 0\text{ V}) = V_{lower\ rail} = -13\text{ V}$

9-7   **a.** $-10.4\text{ V} \leq V_{in} \leq +11\text{ V}$ **b.** noninverting comparator,
      0 V crossover (-13 V for $V_{error} < 0$ V, $+13$ V for $V_{error} > 0$ V)

9-8   **a.** $-11\text{ V to} + 11\text{ V}$ **b.** inverting comparator,
      0 V crossover (-13 V for $V_{error} > 0$ V, $+13$ V for $V_{error} < 0$ V)

9-9 $R_1 = \dfrac{15\text{ V} \times 1\text{ k}\Omega}{5\text{ V}} - 1\text{ k}\Omega = 2\text{ k}\Omega,$ inverting

9-10 $R_1 = \dfrac{15\text{ V} - 5\text{ V}}{10\text{ mA}} - 1\text{ k}\Omega = 1\text{ k}\Omega$, inverting

9-11   **a.** $100°\text{F} = \dfrac{10\text{ mV}}{°\text{F}} = 1\text{ V}$ **b.** $R_{\text{pot bottom}} = \dfrac{1\text{ V} \times 20\text{ k}\Omega}{12\text{ V}} = 1.67\text{ k}\Omega,$

c. red, $I_{\text{Red}} = \dfrac{(12\text{ V} - 2\text{ V}) - 2\text{ V}}{1\text{ k}\Omega} = 8\text{ mA}$; green, $I_{\text{Green}} = \dfrac{(12\text{ V} - 2\text{ V}) - 2\text{ V}}{1.5\text{ k}\Omega} = 5.33\text{ mA},$

d. T > 100°F

9-12   **a.** $I_{\text{Ri}} = \dfrac{13\text{ V} - 3\text{ V}}{1\text{ k}\Omega + 9\text{ k}\Omega} = \dfrac{10\text{ V}}{10\text{ k}\Omega} = 1\text{ mA}$, $V_{\text{Ri}} = 1\text{ k}\Omega \times 1\text{ mA} = 1\text{ V}$, $V_{\text{error}} = 3\text{ V} + 1\text{ V} = 4\text{ V},$

b. $I_{\text{Ri}} = \dfrac{13\text{ V}}{9\text{ k}\Omega} = 1.44\text{ mA}$, $V_{\text{in}} = 0\text{ V} - 1.44\text{ mA} \times 1\text{ k}\Omega = -1.44\text{ V}$

9-13   **a.** $I_{\text{Ri}} = \dfrac{-3\text{ V} - (-13)\text{ V}}{1\text{ k}\Omega + 9\text{ k}\Omega} = \dfrac{10\text{ V}}{10\text{ k}\Omega} = 1\text{ mA}$, $V_{\text{Ri}} = 1\text{ k}\Omega \times 1\text{ mA} = 1\text{ V},$

$V_{\text{error}} = -3\text{ V} - 1\text{ V} = -4\text{ V},$ **b.** $V_{\text{in}} = 0\text{ V} + 1.44\text{ mA} \times 1\text{ k}\Omega = +1.44\text{ V}$

9-14   **a.** $I = \dfrac{13\text{ V}}{10\text{ k}\Omega} = 1.3\text{ mA}$, $V_{\text{Ri}} = 1\text{ k}\Omega \times 1.3\text{ mA} = 1.3\text{ V}$, $V_{\text{error}} = 1.3\text{ V} - 3\text{ V} = -1.7\text{ V},$

b. $V_{\text{in}} = V_{\text{a}} = 0 + 1.3\text{ V} = 1.3\text{ V}$

9-15   **a.** $I = \dfrac{13\text{ V}}{10\text{ k}\Omega} = 1.3\text{ mA}$, $V_{\text{Ri}} = 1\text{ k}\Omega \times 1.3\text{ mA} = 1.3\text{ V}$, $V_{\text{error}} = -1.3\text{ V} - (-3\text{ V}) = 1.7\text{ V},$

b. $V_{\text{in}} = V_{\text{a}} = 0 - 1.3\text{ V} = -1.3\text{ V}$

9-16   Noninverting voltage follower (negative feedback), $V_{\text{a}} = 5\text{ V}$, $V_{\text{out}} = 5\text{ V}$, $V_{\text{error}} = 50\ \mu\text{V}$

9-17   Noninverting voltage amplifier (negative feedback). $R_{\text{amp input}} = \dfrac{500\text{ mV}}{0\text{ A}} = \infty\ \Omega,$

$V_{\text{a}} = V_{\text{in}} = 500\text{ mV}$, $I_{\text{Ri}} = \dfrac{500\text{ mV}}{1\text{ k}\Omega} = 500\ \mu\text{A},$

$I_{Rf} = I_i = 500~\mu A$, $V_{Rf} = 9~k\Omega \times 500~\mu A = 4.5~V$, $V_{out} = 0.5~V + 4.5~V = 5~V$,

$V_{load} = V_{out} = 5~V$, $I_{load} = \dfrac{5~V}{5~k\Omega} = 1~mA$, $I_{out~op~amp} = 1~mA + 500~\mu A = 1.5~mA < 5~mA$, therefore

there are no op amp limitations reached.

9-18 $V_a = V_{in} = 500~mV$, $I_{Ri} = \dfrac{500~mV}{1~k\Omega} = 500~\mu A$, $I_{Rf} = I_{Ri} = 500~\mu A$,

$V_{Rf} = 9~k\Omega \times 500~\mu A = 4.5~V$, $V_{out} = 0.5~V + 4.5~V = 5~V$, $V_{load} = V_{out} = 5~V$,

$I_{load} = \dfrac{5~V}{10~\Omega} = 500~mA$, $I_{out~op~amp} = 500~mA + 500~\mu A = 500.5~mA > 5~mA$, unsafe op amp limi-

tations reached, namely the op amp output current

9-19 $I_B = \dfrac{500.5~mA}{30+1} = 16.14~mA > 10~mA$ so needs a BJT with higher β for this to be reasonable

9-20 Inverting voltage amplifier (negative feedback). $V_a = 0~V$, $I_{Ri} = \dfrac{500~mV - 0~V}{1~k\Omega} = 500~\mu A$,

$I_{Rf} = I_{Ri} = 500~\mu A$, $V_{Rf} = 9~k\Omega \times 500~\mu A = 4.5~V$, $V_{out} = 0~V - 4.5~V = -4.5~V$,

$V_{load} = V_{out} = 4.5~V$, $I_{load} = \dfrac{4.5~V}{5~k\Omega} = 900~\mu A$, $R_{amp~input} = \dfrac{500~mV}{0~A} = \infty~\Omega$

$I_{out~op~amp} = 500~\mu A + 900~\mu A = 1.4~mA < 10~mA$, no op amp limitations reached

9-21 $V_a = 0~V$, $I_{Ri} = \dfrac{2~V - 0~V}{1~k\Omega} = 2~mA$, $I_{Rf} = I_{Ri} = 2~mA$, $V_{Rf} = 9~k\Omega \times 2~mA = 18~V$,

$V_{out} = 0~V - 18~V = -18~V$, $V_{load} = V_{out} = 18~V$ (hits upper rail at +13 V), op amp in saturation

and is no longer acting as an amplifier so none of the calculated values are valid since $V_{error} \neq 0~V$.

9-22 $V_{out} = -(16.67~mA \times 60~k\Omega)$ to $-(33.3~mA \times 60~k\Omega) = -1~V$ to $-2~V$

9-23 $V_{LM} = 82~F~(10~mV~/~F) = 820~mV$, $I_{LM} = 820~mV/1.8~k\Omega = 456~\mu A$,
$I_{ref} = -320~mV/1.8~k\Omega = -178~\mu A$, $I_{in~net} = 456~\mu A - 178~\mu A = 278~\mu A$,

$V_{1\_out} = 0~V - 278~\mu A \times 1~k\Omega = -278~mV$, $I_{1\_out} = \dfrac{278~mV}{10~k\Omega} = 27.8~\mu A$,

$V_{out} = 27.8~\mu A \times 10~k\Omega = 278~mV$, $T_{out} = \dfrac{278~mV}{10~mV/^{\circ}C} = 27.8~^{\circ}C$

9-24   *Signal*:

$$V_b = V_a = \left(\frac{10 \text{ k}\Omega}{11 \text{ k}\Omega}\right) 100 \text{ mV} = 90.9 \text{ mV}, \quad i_{Rf} = i_{Ri} = \frac{90.91 \text{ mV} - (-100 \text{ mV})}{1 \text{ k}\Omega} = 190.91 \text{ μA},$$

$$V_{Rf} = 190.91 \text{ mA} \times 10 \text{ k}\Omega = 1.9091 \text{ V}, \quad V_{\text{out signal}} = 0.0909 \text{ V} + 1.9091 \text{ V} = 2 \text{ V};$$

Noise:

$$V_b = V_a = \left(\frac{10 \text{ k}\Omega}{11 \text{ k}\Omega}\right) 2 \text{ V} = 1.818 \text{ V}, \quad i_{Rf} = i_{Ri} = \frac{1.818 \text{ V} - (2 \text{ V})}{1 \text{ k}\Omega} = 182 \text{ μA},$$

$$V_{Rf} = 182 \text{ μA} \times 10 \text{ k}\Omega = 1.82 \text{ V}, \quad V_{\text{out noise}} = 1.82 \text{ V} - 1.82 \text{ V} = 0 \text{ V}; \text{ ideally 0 V};$$

Signal-to-noise ratio: $\dfrac{v_{\text{out signal}}}{v_{\text{out noise}}} = \dfrac{2 \text{ V}}{0 \text{ V}} = \infty$ is ideally infinite

Chapter 10

10-1   **a.** 12 V, **b.** $I_1 = 6 \text{ A} + 6 \text{ A} = 12 \text{ A}$, $I_2 = 6 \text{ A} + 6 \text{ A} = 12 \text{ A}$, $I_{\text{supply}} = 12 \text{ A} + 12 \text{ A} = 24 \text{ A}$,

    c. $R = \dfrac{12 \text{ V}}{6 \text{ A}} 2 \text{ }\Omega$, **d.** $R_T = \dfrac{12 \text{ V}}{24 \text{ A}} = 0.5 \text{ }\Omega$ **e.** $G_T = \dfrac{1}{0.5 \text{ }\Omega} = 2 \text{ S}$

10-2   **a.** 12 V, **b.** $I_{L1} = \dfrac{24 \text{ W}}{12 \text{ V}} = 2 \text{ A}$, $I_{L2} = I_{L1} = 2 \text{ A}$, $I_1 = 2 \text{ A} + 2 \text{ A} = 4 \text{ A}$, $I_{L3} = \dfrac{60 \text{ W}}{12 \text{ V}} = 5 \text{ A}$,

    $I_{L4} = I_{L3} = 5 \text{ A}$, $I_2 = 5 \text{ A} + 5 \text{ A} = 10 \text{ A}$, $I_{\text{supply}} = 10 \text{ A} + 4 \text{ A} = 14 \text{ A}$, **c.** $R_{L1} = \dfrac{12 \text{ V}}{2 \text{ A}} = 6 \text{ }\Omega$,

    $R_{L2} = R_{L1} = 6 \text{ }\Omega$, $R_{L3} = \dfrac{12 \text{ V}}{5 \text{ A}} = 2.4 \text{ }\Omega$, $R_{L4} = R_{L3} = 2.4 \text{ }\Omega$, **d.** $R_T = \dfrac{12 \text{ V}}{14 \text{ A}} = 0.858 \text{ }\Omega$,

    e. $G_T = \dfrac{14 \text{ A}}{12 \text{ V}} = 1.167 \text{ S}$

10-3   **a.** 15 V, **b.** $I_{R1} = \dfrac{15 \text{ V}}{1 \text{ k}\Omega} = 15 \text{ mA}$, $I_{R2} = \dfrac{15 \text{ V}}{2.2 \text{ k}\Omega} = 6.818 \text{ mA}$, $I_{R3} = \dfrac{15 \text{ V}}{3.3 \text{ k}\Omega} = 4.545 \text{ mA}$,

    c. $I_{\text{supply}} = 15 \text{ mA} + 6.82 \text{ mA} + 4.55 \text{ mA} = 26.36 \text{ mA}$, **d.** $R_T = \dfrac{15 \text{ V}}{26.36 \text{ mA}} = 569 \text{ }\Omega$,

    e. $G_T = \dfrac{1}{569 \text{ }\Omega} = 1.758 \text{ mS}$

10-4 **a.** 15 V, **b.** $I_{R1} = \dfrac{15 \text{ V}}{2.2 \text{ k}\Omega} = 6.818 \text{ mA}$, $I_{R2} = I_{R1} = 6.818 \text{ mA}$, $I_{R3} = \dfrac{15 \text{ V}}{3.3 \text{ k}\Omega} = 4.545 \text{ mA}$,

$I_{R4} = I_{R3} = 4.545 \text{ mA}$, $I_{R5} = I_{R4} = 4.545 \text{ mA}$, **c.** $I_1 = 6.818 \text{ mA} + 6.818 \text{ mA} = 13.64 \text{ mA}$,

$I_2 = 4.545 \text{ mA} + 4.545 \text{ mA} = 9.090 \text{ mA}$, $I_3 = 4.545 \text{ mA} + 9.09 \text{ mA} = 13.64 \text{ mA}$,

$I_{\text{supply}} = 13.64 \text{ mA} + 13.64 \text{ mA} = 27.27 \text{ mA}$, **d.** $R_T = \dfrac{15 \text{ V}}{27.27 \text{ mA}} = 550 \text{ }\Omega$,

e. $R_{3,4,5} = \dfrac{15 \text{ V}}{13.64 \text{ mA}} = 1.1 \text{ k}\Omega$, **f.** $G_T = \dfrac{27.27 \text{ mA}}{15 \text{ V}} = 1.818 \text{ mS}$

10-5 **a.** $R = \dfrac{12 \text{ V}}{6 \text{ A}} = 2 \text{ }\Omega$, **b.** $R_T = \dfrac{2 \text{ }\Omega}{4} = 0.5 \text{ }\Omega$, **c.** $R_{I1} = 0.5 \text{ }\Omega + 0.5 \text{ }\Omega = 1 \text{ }\Omega$, **d.** $G = \dfrac{1}{2\Omega} = 0.5 \text{ S}$,

e. $G_T = 0.5 \text{ S} \times 4 = 2 \text{ S}$, **f.** $G_{I1} = 0.5 \text{ S} + 0.5 \text{ S} = 1 \text{ S}$

10-6 **a.** $G_{L1} = \dfrac{1}{6 \text{ }\Omega} = 166.7 \text{ mS}$, $G_{L2} = G_{L1} = 166.7 \text{ mS}$, $G_{L3} = \dfrac{1}{2.4 \text{ }\Omega} = 416.7 \text{ mS}$,

$G_{L4} = G_{L3} = 416.7 \text{ mS}$, **b.** $G_T = (2 \times 166.7 \text{ mS}) + (2 \times 416.7 \text{ mS}) 1.167 \text{ mS}$,

c. $R_T = \dfrac{1}{1.1667 \text{ S}} = 0.8571 \text{ }\Omega$, **d.** $I_{\text{supply}} = \dfrac{12 \text{ V}}{858 \text{ mS}} = 14 \text{ A}$, **e.** $P_T = 12 \text{ V} \times 14 \text{ A} = 168 \text{ W}$,

f. $P_T = 2(24 \text{ W}) + 2(60 \text{ W}) = 168 \text{ W}$, **g.** yes

10-7 **a.** $R_T = \left((1 \text{ k}\Omega)^{-1} + (2.2 \text{ k}\Omega)^{-1} + (3.3 \text{ k}\Omega)^{-1} \right)^{-1} = 569 \text{ }\Omega$, **b.** $I_{\text{supply}} = \dfrac{15 \text{ V}}{569 \text{ }\Omega} = 26.36 \text{ mA}$,

c. $P = 15 \text{ V} \times 26.4 \text{ mA} = 395.5 \text{ mW}$, **d.** $P_{R1} = \dfrac{15 \text{ V}^2}{1 \text{ k}\Omega} = 225 \text{ mW}$, $P_{R2} = \dfrac{15 \text{ V}^2}{2.2 \text{ k}\Omega} = 102.3 \text{ mW}$,

$P_{R3} = \dfrac{15 \text{ V}^2}{3.3 \text{ k}\Omega} = 68.2 \text{ mW}$, **e.** $P_T = 225 \text{ mW} + 102.3 \text{ mW} + 68.2 \text{ mW} = 395.5 \text{ mW}$, **f.** yes

10-8 $R_4 = \dfrac{1}{3.891 \text{ mS} - 1 \text{ mS} - 455 \text{ }\mu\text{S} - 303 \text{ }\mu\text{S}} = 470 \text{ }\Omega$

10-9 $I_1 = 400 \text{ mA} \times \dfrac{1.37 \text{ k}\Omega}{2.7 \text{ k}\Omega} = 202.8 \text{ mA}$, $I_2 = (400 \text{ mA} - 203 \text{ mA}) \times \dfrac{2.78 \text{ k}\Omega}{4.7 \text{ k}\Omega} = 116.6 \text{ mA}$,

$I_3 = 400 \text{ mA} - 203 \text{ mA} - 117 \text{ mA} = 80.6 \text{ mA}$, currents sum to 400 mA

10-10 $I_X = 400 \text{ mA} \times \dfrac{1.37 \text{ k}\Omega}{2.78 \text{ k}\Omega} = 197.2 \text{ mA}$

10-11 **a.** $R_T = \left((100 \ \Omega)^{-1} + (270 \ \Omega)^{-1} + (470 \ \Omega)^{-1}\right)^{-1} = 63.16 \ \Omega$, **b.** $I = \dfrac{15 \text{ V}}{63.2 \ \Omega} = 237.5 \text{ mA}$,

c. $I_{R1} = 237 \text{ mA} \times \dfrac{63.2 \ \Omega}{100 \ \Omega} = 150 \text{ mA}$

10-12 **a.** $G_T = \dfrac{1}{100 \ \Omega} + \dfrac{1}{270 \ \Omega} + \dfrac{1}{470 \ \Omega} = 15.83 \text{ mS}$ **b.** $I_{supply} = 15.83 \text{ mA} \times 15 \text{ V} = 237.45 \text{ mA}$

c. $G_{R1} = \dfrac{1}{100 \ \Omega} = 10 \text{ mS}$, **d.** $I_{R1} = \dfrac{10 \text{ mS}}{100 \ \Omega} \times 237.5 \text{ mA} = 150 \text{ mA}$

10-13 **a.** 1 mA **b.** $V_R = 1 \text{ mA} \times 0 \ \Omega = 0 \text{ V}$, **c.** $V_R = 1 \text{ mA} \times 1 \ \Omega = 1 \text{ mV}$, **d.** $V_R = 1 \text{ mA} \times 1 \text{ k}\Omega = 1 \text{ V}$,
e. $V_R = 1 \text{ mA} \times 1 \text{ M}\Omega = 1 \text{ kV}$, **f.** $V_R = 1 \text{ mA} \times 1 \text{ G}\Omega = 1 \text{ MV}$, **g.** $V_R = 1 \text{ mA} \times \infty \ \Omega = \infty \text{ V}$ (not really), **h.** No, circuit limitation or component limitation will be reached (perhaps arcing, the breaking down of air like a lightning strike)

10-14 **a.** $V_{R1} = 4 \text{ mA} \times 100 \ \Omega = 400 \text{ mV}$, $V_{R2} = 4 \text{ mA} \times 270 \ \Omega = 1.08 \text{ V}$,

$V_{R3} = 4 \text{ mA} \times 330 \ \Omega = 1.32 \text{ V}$, **b.** $E = 400 \text{ mV} + 1.08 \text{ mV} + 1.32 \text{ mV} = 2.8 \text{ V}$,
c. $P_T = 2.8 \text{ V} \times 4 \text{ mA} = 11.2 \text{ mW}$

10-15 **a.** 20 mA **b.** $I_L = 20 \text{ mA} \times \dfrac{\dfrac{100 \text{ k}\Omega \times 1 \ \Omega}{100 \text{ k}\Omega + 1 \ \Omega}}{1 \ \Omega} = 19.9998 \text{ mA}$

c. $I_L = 20 \text{ mA} \times \dfrac{\dfrac{100 \text{ k}\Omega \times 10 \text{ }\Omega}{100 \text{ k}\Omega + 10 \text{ }\Omega}}{10 \text{ }\Omega} = 19.998 \text{ mA}$ **d.** $I_L = 20 \text{ mA} \times \dfrac{\dfrac{100 \text{ k}\Omega \times 100 \text{ }\Omega}{100 \text{ k}\Omega + 100 \text{ }\Omega}}{100 \text{ }\Omega} = 19.98 \text{ mA}$

e. $I_L = 20 \text{ mA} \times \dfrac{\dfrac{100 \text{ k}\Omega \times 1 \text{ k}\Omega}{100 \text{ k}\Omega + 1 \text{ k}\Omega}}{1 \text{ k}\Omega} = 19.8 \text{ mA}$ **f.** $I_L = 20 \text{ mA} \times \dfrac{\dfrac{100 \text{ k}\Omega \times 10 \text{ k}\Omega}{100 \text{ k}\Omega + 10 \text{ k}\Omega}}{10 \text{ k}\Omega} = 18.18 \text{ mA}$

g. $I_L = \dfrac{20 \text{ mA}}{2} = 10 \text{ mA}$,   **h.** between 10 k$\Omega$ and 100 kΩ

10-16   **a.** $V_E = 5 \text{ V} - 0.7 \text{ V} = 4.3 \text{ V}$,   **b.** $I_E = I_C = \dfrac{4.3 \text{ V}}{2.2 \text{ k}\Omega} = 1.955 \text{ mA}$,

c. $V_C = +15 \text{ V} - (1.955 \text{ mA} \times 4.7 \text{ k}\Omega) = 5.812 \text{ V}$,   **d.** $V_{CE} = 5.814 \text{ V} - 4.3 \text{ V} = 1.51 \text{ V}$,

e. $V_{BE} = 0.7 \text{ V}$ ideal supply, $I_C = 1.955 \text{ mA}$ ideal current supply

10-17   **a.** $I_{supply} = 9 \text{ mA} - 5 \text{ mA} + 2 \text{ mA} = 6 \text{ mA}$, into top node   **b.** $I_{load} = I_{supply} = 6 \text{ mA}$,

c. $V_L = 6 \text{ mA} \times 1 \text{ k}\Omega = 6 \text{ V}$,   **d.** $P_L = 6 \text{ V} \times 6 \text{ mA} = 36 \text{ mW}$

10-18   **a.** 6 mA into top node, 10 kΩ parallel resistance,   **b.** $I_{supply} = 6 \text{ mA} \times \dfrac{10 \text{ k}\Omega}{1 \text{ k}\Omega + 10 \text{ k}\Omega} = 5.455 \text{ mA}$,

c. $I_{load} = I_{supply} = 5.455 \text{ mA}$,   **d.** $V_L = 5.455 \text{ mA} \times 1 \text{ k}\Omega = 5.455 \text{ V}$,

e. $P_{load} = 5.455 \text{ V} \times 5.455 \text{ mA} = 29.75 \text{ mW}$

10-19   **a.** $I_{test \ load} = \left(\dfrac{R_N}{R_N + 1 \text{ k}\Omega} \right) 10 \text{ mA} = 9.9 \text{ mA}$; $R_N = 99 \text{ k}\Omega$; 10 mA source with parallel 99 kΩ re-

sistance   **b.** $I_{load} = 10 \text{ mA} \times \dfrac{4.487 \text{ k}\Omega}{4.7 \text{ k}\Omega} = 9.547 \text{ mA}$, $V_{load} = 9.55 \text{ mA} \times 4.7 \text{ k}\Omega = 44.87 \text{ V}$

10-20   **a.** $R_N = \dfrac{10 \text{ V}}{100 \text{ mA} - 99 \text{ mA}} = 10 \text{ k}\Omega$; 100 mA current source with parallel 10 kΩ resistance,

b. $I_{load} = 100 \text{ mA} \times \dfrac{10 \text{ k}\Omega}{10 \text{ k}\Omega + 10 \text{ }\Omega} = 99.9 \text{ mA}$, $V_{load} = 99.9 \text{ mA} \times 10 \Omega = 0.999 \text{ V}$

10-21 $E_{Th} = 1 \text{ mA} \times 10 \text{ k}\Omega = 10 \text{ V}$ in series with 10 kΩ

10-22 $I_N = \dfrac{10 \text{ V}}{1 \text{ k}\Omega} = 10 \text{ mA}$ in parallel 1 kΩ

10-23 **a.** $E_{Th} = 12 \text{ μA} \times 3 \text{ k}\Omega = 36 \text{ V}$ in series with 3 kΩ, **b.** $I_{R2} = \dfrac{36 \text{ V} - 9 \text{ V}}{3 \text{ k}\Omega + 6 \text{ k}\Omega} = \dfrac{27 \text{ V}}{9 \text{ k}\Omega} = 3 \text{ mA}$,

$V_{R2} = 3 \text{ mA} \times 6 \text{ k}\Omega = 18 \text{ V}$, **c.** $I_{R1} = 6 \text{ mA} \times \dfrac{2 \text{ k}\Omega}{6 \text{ k}\Omega} = 9 \text{ mA}$, $V_{R1} = 9 \text{ mA} \times 3 \text{ k}\Omega = 27 \text{ V}$,

d. $V_{supply} = V_{R1} = 27 \text{ V}$

10-24 **a.** 1.5 mA in parallel with 6 kΩ, **b.** $I_{R1} = (12 \text{ mA} + 1.5 \text{ mA}) \times \dfrac{6 \text{ k}\Omega}{9 \text{ k}\Omega} = 9 \text{ mA}$,

$V_{R1} = 9 \text{ mA} \times 3 \text{ k}\Omega = 27 \text{ V}$, **c.** $I_{R2} = 12 \text{ mA} - 9 \text{ mA} = 3 \text{ mA}$, $V_{R2} = 3 \text{ mA} \times 6 \text{ k}\Omega = 18 \text{ V}$,

d. $I_{voltage\ supply} = I_{R2} = 3 \text{ mA}$

10-25 **a.** $I_{R1} = 6 \text{ mA} \times \dfrac{2 \text{ k}\Omega}{3 \text{ k}\Omega} = 4 \text{ mA}$, $I_{R2} = 6 \text{ mA} \times \dfrac{2 \text{ k}\Omega}{6 \text{ k}\Omega} = 2 \text{ mA}$, **b.** $I_{supply} = \dfrac{12 \text{ V}}{2 \text{ k}\Omega} = 6 \text{ mA}$,

c. $I_{volt\ supply} = \dfrac{6 \text{ mA}}{3} = 2 \text{ mA}$, **d.** $V_{R1} = V_{R2} = 12 \text{ V}$

10-26 The 11 V supply loads down the 12 V supplies and pulls both down to 11 V

Chapter 11

11-1 **a.** 1 and 2 **b.** 3 and 4
  c. 1 with 2 with 3//4 combination with 5

11-2 **a.** 1 and 2 **b.** 3 and 4
  c. 1, 2, 3//4 combination with 5 with 6

11-3 $R_A = 1 \text{ k}\Omega + 1.8 \text{ k}\Omega + 2.7 \text{ k}\Omega = 5.5 \text{ k}\Omega$

11-4 $R_B = \left((1 \text{ k}\Omega)^{-1} + (1.8 \text{ k}\Omega)^{-1} + (2.7 \text{ k}\Omega)^{-1} \right)^{-1} = 519 \text{ }\Omega$

11-5 **a.** $R_A = \left((3 \text{ k}\Omega // 6 \text{ k}\Omega) + 1 \text{ k}\Omega \right) // (2 \text{ k}\Omega + 4 \text{ k}\Omega + 6 \text{ k}\Omega) = (2 \text{ k}\Omega + 1 \text{ k}\Omega) // (12 \text{ k}\Omega) = $
  $2.4 \text{ k}\Omega$, **b.** $R_A = (1 \text{ k}\Omega) // (2 \text{ k}\Omega + 4 \text{ k}\Omega + 6 \text{ k}\Omega) = (1 \text{ k}\Omega) // (12 \text{ k}\Omega) = 923 \text{ }\Omega$,

  c. $R_A = (3 \text{ k}\Omega // 6 \text{ k}\Omega) + 1 \text{ k}\Omega = 2 \text{ k}\Omega + 1 \text{ k}\Omega = 3 \text{ k}\Omega$

11-6 **a.** $R_{\text{B}} = 1\ \text{k}\Omega + 6\ \text{k}\Omega // 12\ \text{k}\Omega + 2\ \text{k}\Omega // 3\ \text{k}\Omega // 6\ \text{k}\Omega + 6\ \text{k}\Omega = 1\ \text{k}\Omega + 4\ \text{k}\Omega + 1\ \text{k}\Omega + 6\ \text{k}\Omega = 12\ \text{k}\Omega$, **b.** $R_{\text{B}} = 1\ \text{k}\Omega + 6\ \text{k}\Omega // 12\ \text{k}\Omega + 6\ \text{k}\Omega = 1\ \text{k}\Omega + 4\ \text{k}\Omega + 6\ \text{k}\Omega = 11\ \text{k}\Omega$,

c. $R_{\text{B}} = 1\ \text{k}\Omega + 6\ \text{k}\Omega // 12\ \text{k}\Omega + 3\ \text{k}\Omega // 6\ \text{k}\Omega + 6\ \text{k}\Omega = 1\ \text{k}\Omega + 4\ \text{k}\Omega + 2\ \text{k}\Omega + 6\ \text{k}\Omega = 13\ \text{k}\Omega$

11-7 **a.** $R_{\text{A}} = 6\ \text{k}\Omega // 6\ \text{k}\Omega // 6\ \text{k}\Omega = 2\ \text{k}\Omega$, **b.** $R_{\text{A}} = 0\ \Omega$ (short), **c.** $R_{\text{A}} = 6\ \text{k}\Omega // 6\ \text{k}\Omega = 3\ \text{k}\Omega$

11-8 **a.** $R_{\text{B}} = 18\ \text{k}\Omega // \left(3\ \text{k}\Omega + \left(8\ \text{k}\Omega // 24\ \text{k}\Omega\right)\right) = 18\ \text{k}\Omega // \left(3\ \text{k}\Omega + 6\ \text{k}\Omega\right) = 6\ \text{k}\Omega$,

b. $R_{\text{B}} = 18\ \text{k}\Omega // 3\ \text{k}\Omega = 2.57\ \text{k}\Omega$, **c.** $R_{\text{B}} = 18\ \text{k}\Omega // \left(3\ \text{k}\Omega + 8\ \text{k}\Omega\right) = 6.83\ \text{k}\Omega$

11-9 **a.** $I_{\text{T}} = \dfrac{36\ \text{V}}{2.4\ \text{k}\Omega} = 15\ \text{mA}$, **b.** $I_{3\text{K}} = \dfrac{24\ \text{V}}{3\ \text{k}\Omega} = 8\ \text{mA}$, $V_{3\text{k}} = 12\ \text{mA} \times 2\ \text{k}\Omega = 24\ \text{V}$,

c. $V_{\text{a}} = 18\ \text{V}$, $V_{\text{b}} = 18\ \text{V} - 24\ \text{V} = -6\ \text{V}$, $V_{\text{e}} = -18\ \text{V}$,

d. $V_{\text{ae}} = 18\ \text{V} - \left(-18\ \text{V}\right) = 36\ \text{V}$, $V_{\text{ab}} = 18\ \text{V} - \left(-6\ \text{V}\right) = 24\ \text{V}$, $V_{\text{bd}} = -6\ \text{V} - \left(-18\ \text{V}\right) = 12\ \text{V}$,

e. $I_{\text{supply}} = \dfrac{36\ \text{V}}{1.714\ \text{k}\Omega} = 21\ \text{mA}$, **f.** $I_{\text{supply}} = \dfrac{36\ \text{V}}{12\ \text{k}\Omega} = 3\ \text{mA}$

11-10 **a.** $I = \dfrac{36\ \text{V} - \left(-36\right)\ \text{V}}{12\ \text{k}\Omega} = 6\ \text{mA}$, **b.** $I_{3\text{k}} = \dfrac{6\ \text{V}}{3\ \text{k}\Omega} = 2\ \text{mA}$, $V_{3\text{k}} = 6\ \text{V}$,

c. $V_{\text{a}} = 36\ \text{V}$, $V_{\text{b}} = 36\ \text{V} - 6\ \text{V} = 30\ \text{V}$, $V_{\text{f}} = -36\ \text{V}$,

d. $V_{\text{af}} = 36\ \text{V} - \left(-36\right)\ \text{V} = 72\ \text{V}$, $V_{\text{ab}} = 36\ \text{V} - 30\ \text{V} = 6\ \text{V}$, $V_{\text{bd}} = 30\ \text{V} - 0\ \text{V} = 30\ \text{V}$,

e. $I = \dfrac{36\ \text{V} - \left(-36\right)\ \text{V}}{12\ \text{k}\Omega} = 9\ \text{mA}$, **f.** $I = \dfrac{36\ \text{V} - \left(-36\right)\ \text{V}}{12\ \text{k}\Omega} = 5.14\ \text{mA}$

11-11 **a.** $I_{\text{supply}} = \dfrac{18\ \text{V}}{1.5\ \text{k}\Omega} = 12\ \text{mA}$, **b.** $I_{4\text{k}} = \dfrac{16\ \text{V}}{4\ \text{k}\Omega} = 4\ \text{mA}$, $V_{4\text{k}} = 9\ \text{V} - 2\ \text{V} - \left(-9\right)\ \text{V} = 16\ \text{V}$,

c. $I_{\text{LED\_L}} = 12\ \text{mA} - 8\ \text{mA} - 1\ \text{mA} = 3\ \text{mA}$, $I_{\text{LED\_R}} = \dfrac{9\ \text{V} - 2\ \text{V} - \left(-9\right)\ \text{V}}{2\ \text{k}\Omega} = \dfrac{16\ \text{V}}{2\ \text{k}\Omega} = 8\ \text{mA}$,

d. $V_{\text{a}} = 9\ \text{V}$, $V_{\text{b}} = 9\ \text{V} - 2\ \text{V} = 7\ \text{V}$, $V_{\text{c}} = 9\ \text{V} - 16\ \text{V} = -7\ \text{V}$, $V_{\text{d}} = -9\ \text{V}$,

e. $V_{\text{ad}} = 9\ \text{V} - \left(-9\right)\ \text{V} = 18\ \text{V}$, $V_{\text{ab}} = 9\ \text{V} - 7\ \text{V} = 2\ \text{V}$, $V_{\text{bc}} = 7\ \text{V} - \left(-7\right)\ \text{V} = 14\ \text{V}$

11-12 **a.** $I_{supply} = \dfrac{16\text{ V} - (-16)\text{ V} - 2\text{ V}}{2\text{ k}\Omega + 3\text{ k}\Omega} = \dfrac{30\text{ V}}{5\text{ k}\Omega} = 6\text{ mA}$, **b.** $I_{supply} = \dfrac{2\text{ V}}{1\text{ k}\Omega} = 2\text{ mA}$, $V_{1k} = 2\text{ V}$

  c. $V_a = 16\text{ V}$, $V_b = 16\text{ V} - 12\text{ V} = 4\text{ V}$, $V_c = 4\text{ V} - 18\text{ V} = -14\text{ V}$, $V_d = -16\text{ V}$,

  d. $V_{ad} = 16\text{ V} - (-16)\text{ V} = 32\text{ V}$, $V_{ac} = 16\text{ V} - (-14)\text{ V} = 30\text{ V}$, $V_{ca} = -30\text{ V}$

11-13 **a.** $R_T = 5\text{ k}\Omega$, **b.** $I = \dfrac{45\text{ V}}{5\text{ k}\Omega} 9\text{ mA}$, **c.** $V_{load} = 1\text{ mA} \times 16\text{ k}\Omega = 16\text{ V}$,

  $I_{load} = 3\text{ mA} \times \dfrac{8\text{ k}\Omega}{24\text{ k}\Omega} = 1\text{ mA}$, **d.** $I = \dfrac{45\text{ V}}{1\text{ k}\Omega} = 45\text{ mA}$; jeopardy: supply, 1 kΩ resistor

11-14 **a.** $R_T = 6\text{ k}\Omega$, **b.** $I_{supply} = \dfrac{54\text{ V}}{6\text{ k}\Omega} = 9\text{ mA}$, **c.** $V_{load} = 1\text{ mA} \times 2\text{ k}\Omega = 2\text{ V}$, $I_{load} = 1\text{ mA}$, **d.** $\infty\text{ A}$

  (really current limited or physically limited); jeopardy: supply, ammeter

11-15 **a.** $E_{Th} = 90\text{ V} \times \dfrac{6\text{ k}\Omega}{9\text{ k}\Omega} = 60\text{ V}$, **b.** $I_N = 18\text{ mA} \times \dfrac{2\text{ k}\Omega}{3\text{ k}\Omega} = 12\text{ mA}$

  c. $R_{Th} = \dfrac{60\text{ V}}{12\text{ mA}} = 5\text{ k}\Omega$ or $R_{Th} = 3\text{ k}\Omega + 6\text{ k}\Omega // 3\text{ k}\Omega = 5\text{ k}\Omega$

  d. $I_{load} = \dfrac{60\text{ V}}{1\text{ k}\Omega + 5\text{ k}\Omega} = 10\text{ mA}$, $V_{load} = 10\text{ mA} \times 1\text{ k}\Omega = 10\text{ V}$,

  e. $I_{load} = \left(\dfrac{5\text{ k}\Omega}{6\text{ k}\Omega}\right) 12\text{ mA} = 10\text{ mA}$, $V_{load} = 10\text{ mA} \times 1\text{ k}\Omega = 10\text{ V}$,

  f. $I_{supply} = \dfrac{90\text{ V}}{3\text{ k}\Omega + 6\text{ k}\Omega // 4\text{ k}\Omega} = 16.67\text{ mA}$, $I_{load} = \left(\dfrac{6\text{ k}\Omega}{4\text{ k}\Omega + 10\text{ k}\Omega}\right) 16.67\text{ mA} = 10\text{ mA}$,

  $V_{load} = 10\text{ mA} \times 1\text{ k}\Omega = 10\text{ V}$, **g.** Thévenin model, Norton model and actual circuit produced the same load current and load voltage.

11-16 **a.** $R_a = R$ **b.** $I_3 = 80\text{ μA}$, $I_2 = 40\text{ μA}$, $I_1 = 20\text{ μA}$, $I_0 = 10\text{ μA}$

11-17 **a.** $I_3 = 160\text{ μA} \times \dfrac{R}{2R} = 80\text{ μA}$, $I_2 = 80\text{ μA} \times \dfrac{R}{2R} = 40\text{ μA}$, $I_1 = 40\text{ μA} \times \dfrac{R}{2R} = 20\text{ μA}$,

  $I_0 = 20\text{ μA} \times \dfrac{R}{2R} = 10\text{ μA}$, **b.** $I_3 = 80\text{ μA}$, $I_{32} = 80\text{ μA} + 40\text{ μA} = 120\text{ μA}$,

$I_{321} = 120 \ \mu A + 20 \ \mu A = 140 \ \mu A$, $I_{3210} = 150 \ \mu A$,

c. $1111_2 = 15 \Rightarrow$ Inverted & Analog $= -150 \ \mu V \Rightarrow$ Amplified by $\times 1000 = -150$ mV

11-18 **a.** $I_3 = 80 \ \mu A$, $I_2 = 0 \ \mu A$, $I_1 = 20 \ \mu A$, $I_0 = 0 \ \mu A$, **b.** $I_3 = 80 \ \mu A$, $I_{32} = 80 \ \mu A$, $I_{321} = 100 \ \mu A$,

$I_{3210} = 100 \ \mu A$, **c.** $V_{out} = 100 \ \mu A \times 1 \ k\Omega = 100$ mV

11-19 $10_{10} = 1010_2 = 100 \ \mu A \times -1000 \ \dfrac{V}{A} = -100$ mV, $9_{10} = 1001_2 = 90 \ \mu A \times -1000 \ \dfrac{V}{A} = -90$ mV,

$7_{10} = 0111_2 = 70 \ \mu A \times -1000 \ \dfrac{V}{A} = -70$ mV

11-20 **a.** $V_a = \left(\dfrac{10 \ k\Omega}{13.3 \ k\Omega} \right) 20 \ V = 15 \ V$, $V_b = \left(\dfrac{1.2 \ k\Omega}{3 \ k\Omega} \right) 20 \ V = 8 \ V$, $V_{ab} = 15.0 \ V - 8.0 \ V = 7.0 \ V$,

b. $R_T = 3.3 \ k\Omega \ // 1.8 \ k\Omega + 10 \ k\Omega \ // \ 1.2 \ k\Omega = 2.236 \ k\Omega$, $I_T = \dfrac{20 \ V}{2.236 \ k\Omega} = 8.945$ mA,

$I_{R1} = 3.158$ mA and $I_{R2} = 0.961$ mA (CDR), $I_{SC} = 3.158 \ mA - 0.961 \ mA = 2.2$ mA,

c. $R_{TH} = \dfrac{7 \ V}{2.197 \ mA} = 3.186 \ k\Omega$, **d.** $I_{load} = \dfrac{7 \ V}{3.186 \ k\Omega + 6.8 \ k\Omega} = 701 \ \mu A$,

$V_{load} = 701 \ \mu A (6.8 \ k\Omega) = 4.77 \ V$, **e.** $I_{load} = \dfrac{7 \ V - 2 \ V}{3.186 \ k\Omega} = 1.57$ mA,

f. $R_2 = \dfrac{1.2 \ k\Omega}{1.8 \ k\Omega} (3.3 \ k\Omega) = 2.2 \ k\Omega$

11-21 **a.** $R_T = 1 \ k\Omega + 13.3 \ k\Omega \ // \ 3 \ k\Omega = 3.448 \ k\Omega$, $I_T = \dfrac{20 \ V}{3.448 \ k\Omega} = 5.80$ mA, $I_{R1} = I_{R2} = 1.068$ mA

(CDR), $I_{R3} = I_{R4} = 4.732$ mA, $V_a = 1.068 \ mA \times 10 \ k\Omega = 10.68 \ V$,

$V_b = 4.732 \ mA \times 1.2 \ k\Omega = 5.68 \ V$, $V_{ab} = 10.68 \ V - 5.68 \ V = 5.00 \ V$,

b. $R_T = 1 \ k\Omega + 3.3 \ k\Omega \ // \ 1.8 \ k\Omega + 10 \ k\Omega \ // 1.2 \ k\Omega = 3.236 \ k\Omega$, $I_T = \dfrac{20 \ V}{3.236 \ k\Omega} = 6.18$ mA,

$I_{R1} = 2.18$ mA (CDR), $I_{R2} = 0.66$ mA $I_{sc} = 2.18 \ mA - 0.66 \ mA = 1.52$ mA,

c. $R_{TH} = \dfrac{5 \ V}{1.519 \ mA} = 3.29 \ k\Omega$,

d. $I_{load} = \dfrac{5.0\ V}{3.29\ k\Omega + 6.8\ k\Omega} = 496\ \mu A,\quad V_{load} = 496\ \mu A \times 6.8\ k\Omega = 3.37\ V,$

e. $I_{load} = \dfrac{5.0\ V - 2.0\ V}{3.29\ k\Omega} = 912\ \mu A,$ **f.** $R_2 = \dfrac{1.2\ k\Omega}{1.8\ k\Omega}(3.3\ k\Omega) = 2.2\ k\Omega$

Chapter 12

12-1 $\ 3\ V_p,\ -3\ V_{min},\ V_{pp} = 3\ V - (-3\ V) = 6\ V_{pp},\ \ 2\ ms,\ \ f = 1/2\ ms = 500\ Hz,\ \ 2\ cycles$

12-2 $\ 2\ mA_p,\ -2\ mA_{min},\ I_{pp} = 2\ mA - (-2)\ mA = 4\ mA_{pp},\ \ 8\ \mu s,\ \ f = 1/8\ \mu s = 125\ kHz,\ \ 1\ cycle$

12-3 $\ \textbf{a.}\ T = \dfrac{1}{100\ Hz} = 10\ ms\ \ \textbf{b.}\ T = \dfrac{1}{5\ MHz} = 200\ ns$

12-4 $\ \textbf{a.}\ T = \dfrac{1}{1\ kHz} = 1\ ms,\ \ \textbf{b.}\ T = \dfrac{1}{2\ GHz} = 500\ ps$

12-5 $\ \textbf{a.}\ f = \dfrac{1}{10\ ms} = 100\ Hz,\ \ \textbf{b.}\ f = \dfrac{1}{33\ ns} = 30.3\ MHz$

12-6 $\ \textbf{a.}\ f = \dfrac{1}{100\ \mu s} = 10\ kHz,\ \ \textbf{b.}\ f = \dfrac{1}{500\ ps} = 2\ GHz$

12-7 $\ \textbf{a.}\ V_{avg} = V_{dc} = \dfrac{A_{net}}{T} = \dfrac{0\ V \cdot ms}{2\ ms} = 0\ V_{dc},\ \ \textbf{b.}\ 6\ V_p,\ 0\ V_{min},\ V_{pp} = 6\ V - (0\ V) = 6\ V_{pp}$

12-8 $\ \textbf{a.}\ i_{dc} = \dfrac{2\ mA_p + (-2\ mA_{min})}{2} = \dfrac{0}{2} = 0\ mA_{dc},\ \ \textbf{b.}\ i_p = 2\ mA_{p\ ac\ only} + 5\ mA_{dc} = 7\ mA_{p\ total\ signal},$

$i_{min} = 5\ mA_{dc} + (-2\ mA_{min\ ac\ only}) = 3\ mA_{min\ total\ signal},\ \ i_{pp} = 7\ mA_{max} - 3\ mA_{min} = 4\ mA_{pp}$

12-9 $\ 4\ V_p,\ -2\ V_{min},\ V_{pp} = 4\ V_p - (-2\ V_{min}) = 6\ V_{pp},\ \ V_{dc} = \dfrac{1}{2}(4\ V_p + (-2\ V_{min})) = \dfrac{2\ V}{2} = 1\ V_{dc}$

12-10 $\ 10\ mA_p,\ 4\ mA_{min},\ i_{pp} = 10\ mA - 4\ mA = 6\ mA_{dc},\ \ i_{dc} = \dfrac{1}{2}(10\ mA + (4\ mA)) = 7\ mA$

12-11 $\ \textbf{a.}\ V_{p\ out} = 45\ V_p \times \dfrac{(12\ k\Omega\,/\!/\,6\ k\Omega)}{(12\ k\Omega\,/\!/\,6\ k\Omega) + 2\ k\Omega} = 45\ V_p \times \dfrac{4\ k\Omega}{6\ k\Omega} = 30\ V_p,$

b. $V_{p\ out} = 45\ V_p \times \dfrac{(6\ k\Omega\ //\ 6\ k\Omega)}{(6\ k\Omega\ //\ 6\ k\Omega) + 2\ k\Omega + 6\ k\Omega} = 45\ V_p \times \dfrac{3\ k\Omega}{11\ k\Omega} = 12.27\ V_p,$

c. $V_{p\ out} = 45\ V_p \times \dfrac{(0\ k\Omega\ //\ 1\ k\Omega)}{(0\ k\Omega\ //\ 6\ k\Omega) + 2\ k\Omega + 12\ k\Omega} = 45\ V_p \times \dfrac{0\ k\Omega}{14\ k\Omega} = 0\ V_p,$

12-12   **a.** $V_{p\ out} = 45\ V_p \times \dfrac{(12\ k\Omega\ //\ 6\ k\Omega)}{(12\ k\Omega\ //\ 6\ k\Omega) + 2\ k\Omega} = 45\ V_p \times \dfrac{4\ k\Omega}{6\ k\Omega} = 30\ V_p,$

b. $V_{p\ out} = 45\ V_p \times \dfrac{(6\ k\Omega\ //\ 6\ k\Omega) + 6\ k\Omega}{(6\ k\Omega\ //\ 6\ k\Omega) + 2\ k\Omega + 6\ k\Omega} = 45\ V_p \times \dfrac{9\ k\Omega}{11\ k\Omega} = 36.82\ V_p,$

c. $V_{p\ out} = 45\ V_p \times \dfrac{12\ k\Omega}{12\ k\Omega + 2\ k\Omega} = 38.57\ V_p$

12-13   **a.** $P_{ave\ out} = \dfrac{\left(\dfrac{30\ V_p}{\sqrt{2}}\right)^2}{6\ k\Omega} = 75\ mW,$ **b.** $P_{ave\ out} = \dfrac{\left(\dfrac{12.27\ V_p}{\sqrt{2}}\right)^2}{6\ k\Omega} = 12.55\ mW,$ **c.** $P_{out\ ave} = 0\ mW$

12-14   **a.** $P_{ave\ supply} = \dfrac{\left(\dfrac{45\ V_p}{\sqrt{2}}\right)^2}{6\ k\Omega} = 168.8\ mW,$ **b.** $P_{supply\ ave} = \dfrac{\left(\dfrac{45\ V_p}{\sqrt{2}}\right)^2}{11\ k\Omega} = 92.05\ mW,$

c. $P_{supply\ ave} = \dfrac{\left(\dfrac{45\ V_p}{\sqrt{2}}\right)^2}{14\ k\Omega} = 72.32\ mW$

12-15   **a.** $V_{p\ load} = \sqrt{2} \times 15\ V_{rms} = 21.21\ V_p,$ **b.** $V_{p\ load} = 21.21\ V_p - 0.7\ V = 20.51\ V_p,$ **c.** half wave,

20.51 V_p, 16.7 ms,   **d.** $I_{p\ load} = \dfrac{20.51\ V_p}{1.8\ k\Omega} = 11.39\ mA_p,$ **e.** half wave, 11.39 mA_p, 16.7 ms,

f. $-21.21\ V_p$

12-16   **a.** 4 V_{pp} **b.** 4 V_{pp}

12-17   **a.** negative feedback,   **b.** Noninverting,   **c.** 100 mV_{rms},   **d.** 100 mV_{rms},

e. $I_{Rf} = \dfrac{100\ V_{rms}}{2.2\ k\Omega} = 45.5\ \mu A_{rms},$ **f.** $V_{Rf} = 45.45\ \mu A_{rms} \times 4.7\ k\Omega = 214\ mV_{rms},$

g. $V_{out} = 100\ mV_{rms} + 214\ mV_{rms} = 314\ mV_{rms}$ noninverted,   **h.** $P_{ave\ Rf} = \dfrac{(214\ mV_{rms})^2}{4.7\ k\Omega} = 9.71\ \mu W$

12-18   **a.** negative feedback, **b.** inverting, **c.** 0 V, **d.** 2.2 V_{rms}, **e.** $I_{Rf} = \dfrac{2.2\ V_{rms}}{2.2\ k\Omega} = 1\ mA_{rms}$, **f.** 4.7 V_{rms},

g. 4.7 V_{rms} inverted, **h.** $P_{ave\ Rf} = 4.7\ V_{rms} \times 1\ mA_{rms} = 4.7\ mW$

12-19   **a.** $V_{load\ 1} = 36\ V \times \dfrac{6\ k\Omega}{3\ k\Omega + 6\ k\Omega} = 24\ V_{dc}$, **b.** $V_{load\ 2} = 1\ mA \times 6\ \Omega = 6\ V_{dc}$,

c. $V_{load} = 24\ V_{dc} + 6\ V_{dc} = 30\ V_{dc}$, **d.** $I_{load} = \dfrac{30\ V_{dc}}{6\ k\Omega} = 5\ mA_{dc}$,

e. $P_{load} = 5\ mA_{dc} \times 30\ V_{dc} = 150\ mW$

12-20   **a.** $I_{load\ 1} = \dfrac{36\ V_{dc}}{6\ k\Omega + 3\ k\Omega} = 4\ mA_{dc}$, **b.** $I_{load\ 2} = -3\ mA \times \dfrac{2\ k\Omega}{3\ k\Omega} = -2\ mA_{dc}$,

c. $I_{load} = 4\ mA_{dc} + (-2)\ mA_{dc} = 2\ mA_{dc}$, **d.** $V_{load} = 2\ mA_{dc} \times 3\ k\Omega = 6\ V_{dc}$,

e. $P_{load} = 2\ mA_{dc} \times 6\ V_{dc} = 12\ mW$

12-21   **a.** $I_{load\ 1} = \dfrac{24\ V_{dc}}{12\ k\Omega} = 2\ mA_{dc}$,   **b.** $I_{load\ 2} = 3\ mA \times \dfrac{1}{3} = -1\ mA_{dc}$,

c. $I_{load\ 3} = 12\ mA \times \dfrac{12\ k\Omega\ //\ 2.4\ k\Omega}{12\ k\Omega} = 2\ mA_{dc}$,

d. $I_{load} = 2\ mA_{dc} + (-1)\ mA_{dc} + 2\ mA_{dc} = 3\ mA_{dc}$, **e.** $V_{load} = 3\ mA_{dc} \times 12\ k\Omega = 36\ V_{dc}$

12-22   **a.** $V_{load\ of\ 36\ V} = 0\ V_{dc}$ **b.** $V_{load\ of\ 12\ V} = 12\ V_{dc}$ **c.** $V_{load} = 12\ V_{dc}$ **d.** $I_{load} = \dfrac{12\ V_{dc}}{6\ k\Omega} = 2\ mA_{dc}$

12-23   **a.** $I_{load\ 1} = 0\ mA_{dc}$, **b.** $I_{load\ 2} = \dfrac{36\ V}{6\ k\Omega + 3\ k\Omega} = 4\ mA_{dc}$, **c.** $I_{load} = 0\ mA_{dc} + 4\ mA_{dc} = 4\ mA_{dc}$,

d. $V_{load} = 4\ mA_{dc} \times 3\ k\Omega = 12\ V_{dc}$

12-24   **a.** $V_{load\ 1} = 25\ V_{rms} \times \dfrac{5\ k\Omega}{5\ k\Omega + 20\ k\Omega} = 5\ V_{rms}$, **b.** $V_{load\ 2} = 8\ mA \times 5\ k\Omega = 40\ V_{rms}$,

c. $V_{load} = 5\ V_{rms} + 40\ V_{rms} = 45\ V_{rms}$, **d.** $I_{load} = \dfrac{45\ V_{rms}}{5\ k\Omega} = 9\ mA_{rms}$,

e. $P_{ave} = 9 \text{ mA}_{rms} \times 45 \text{ V}_{rms} = 405 \text{ mW}$, **f.** $V_{p \text{ load}} = \sqrt{2} \times 45 \text{ V}_{rms} = 63.6 \text{ V}_p$,

g. $i_{p \text{ load}} = \sqrt{2} \times 9 \text{ mA}_{rms} = 12.7 \text{ mA}_p$

12-25 **a.** $I_{\text{load 1}} = 0 \text{ mA}_{rms}$, **b.** $I_{\text{load 2}} = 10 \text{ mA}_{rms}$, **c.** $I_{\text{load}} = 0 \text{ mA}_{rms} + 10 \text{ mA}_{rms} = 10 \text{ mA}_{rms}$,

d. $V_{\text{load}} = 10 \text{ mA}_{rms} \times 5 \text{ k}\Omega = 50 \text{ V}_{rms}$, **e.** $P_{ave} = (10 \text{ mA}_{rms})^2 \times 5 \text{ k}\Omega = 500 \text{ mW}$,

f. $V_{p \text{ load}} = \sqrt{2} \times 50 \text{ V}_{rms} = 70.7 \text{ V}_p$, **g.** $I_{p \text{ load}} = \sqrt{2} \times 10 \text{ mA}_{rms} = 14.1 \text{ mA}_p$

12-26 **a.** $V_{\text{load of dc}} = 36 \text{ V} \times \dfrac{3 \text{k}\Omega}{6 \text{ k}\Omega + 3 \text{ k}\Omega} = 12 \text{ V}_{dc}$, **b.** $V_{\text{load of ac}} = 6 \text{ mA}_{rms} \times 6 \text{ k}\Omega // 3 \text{ k}\Omega = 12 \text{ V}_{rms}$,

c. $V_{\text{rms total signal}} = \sqrt{12 \text{ V}_{rms}{}^2 + 12 \text{ V}_{dc}{}^2} = 16.97 \text{ V}_{rms}$, **d.** $P_{\text{ave total signal}} = \dfrac{(16.97 \text{ V}_{rms})^2}{3 \text{ k}\Omega} = 96 \text{ mW}$,

e. sine wave, 28.97 V_{max}, -4.97 V_{min}, period: 1 ms

12-27 **a.** $I_{\text{load of dc}} = -5 \text{ mA}_{dc} \times \dfrac{5 \text{ k}\Omega}{25 \text{ k}\Omega} = -1 \text{ mA}_{dc}$,

b. $I_{\text{load of ac}} = \dfrac{100 \text{ V}_{rms}}{25 \text{ k}\Omega} = 4 \text{ mA}_{rms}$,

c. $I_{\text{rms total signal}} = \sqrt{(4 \text{ mA}_{rms})^2 + (-1 \text{ mA}_{dc})^2} = 4.123 \text{ mA}_{rms}$,

d. $P_{\text{ave total signal}} = (4.123 \text{ mA}_{rms})^2 \times 20 \text{ k}\Omega = 340 \text{ mW}$, **e.** sine wave, 4.66 mA_{max}, -6.66 mA_{min}, period: 1 ms

12-28 **a.** $V_{\text{out 1}} = -150 \text{ mV}_{dc} \times \dfrac{6 \text{ k}\Omega}{1 \text{k}\Omega} = -900 \text{ mV}_{dc}$, **b.** $V_{\text{out 2}} = -200 \text{ mV}_{dc} \times \dfrac{6 \text{ k}\Omega}{2 \text{k}\Omega} = -600 \text{ mV}_{dc}$,

c. $V_{\text{out 3}} = -250 \text{ mV}_{dc} \times \dfrac{6 \text{ k}\Omega}{3 \text{k}\Omega} = -500 \text{ mV}_{dc}$,

d. $V_{\text{out}} = -900 \text{ mV} - 600 \text{ mV} - 500 \text{ mV} = -2 \text{ V}_{dc}$

12-29 **a.** $V_{\text{out 1}} = -150 \text{ mV}_{dc} \times \dfrac{6 \text{ k}\Omega}{1 \text{k}\Omega} = -900 \text{ mV}_{dc}$, **b.** $V_{\text{out 2}} = -(-200 \text{ mV}_{dc}) \times \dfrac{6 \text{ k}\Omega}{2 \text{k}\Omega} = +600 \text{ mV}_{dc}$,

c. $V_{\text{out 3}} = -250 \text{ mV}_{dc} \times \dfrac{6 \text{ k}\Omega}{3 \text{k}\Omega} = -500 \text{ mV}_{dc}$,

d. $V_{\text{out}} = -900 \text{ mV} + 600 \text{ mV} - 500 \text{ mV} = -800 \text{ mV}_{dc}$

12-30   **a.** $V_{\text{out of dc}} = -5\ V_{\text{dc}} \times \dfrac{100\ k\Omega}{100\ k\Omega} = -5\ V_{\text{dc}},$ **b.** $V_{\text{out of ac}} = -141\ mV_{\text{rms}} \times \dfrac{100\ k\Omega}{10\ k\Omega} = 1.414\ V_{\text{rms}}$ in-

verted sine wave, **c.** $V_P = 1.414\ V_{\text{rms}} \times \sqrt{2} = 4\ V_{\text{pp}},$ **d.** inverted sine wave with 2 V_{max}, $-2\ V_{\text{min}}$, T of 2 ms, **e.** inverted sine wave with $-3\ V_{\text{max}}$, $-7\ V_{\text{min}}$, $-5\ V_{\text{dc}}$, T of 2 ms,

f. $V_{\text{rms total signal}} = \sqrt{\left(-1.414\ V_{\text{rms}}\right)^2 + \left(5\ V_{\text{dc}}\right)^2} = 5.20\ V_{\text{rms}}$

12-31   **a.** $V_{\text{rms}} = \dfrac{\dfrac{5\ V_{\text{pp}}}{2}}{\sqrt{2}} = 1.767\ V_{\text{rms}},$ **b.** $V_{\text{rms}} = \dfrac{\dfrac{5\ V_{\text{pp}}}{2}}{\sqrt{2}} = 1.767\ V_{\text{rms}},$

c. $V_{\text{rms}} = \sqrt{\left(1.767\ V_{\text{rms}}\right)^2 + \left(5\ V_{\text{dc}}\right)^2} = 5.303\ V_{\text{rms}}$

12-32   **a.** $V_{\text{rms}} = \dfrac{\dfrac{5\ V_{\text{pp}}}{2}}{\sqrt{2}} = 1.768\ V_{\text{rms}},$ **b.** $V_{\text{rms}} = \dfrac{5\ V_p}{\sqrt{3}} = 1.443\ V_{\text{rms}},$

c. $V_{\text{rms}} = \sqrt{\left(1.443\ V_{\text{rms}}\right)^2 + \left(10\ V_{\text{dc}}\right)^2} = 10.104\ V_{\text{rms}}$

Chapter 13

13-1   **a.** 0 A, **b.** cosine wave, $I_{p\,C} = 2\pi \times 100\ Hz \times 1\ \mu F = 628\ \mu A_p,$

c. square wave, $I_{p\,C} = 1\ \mu F \times \left[\dfrac{10\ V}{2.5\ ms}\right] = 4\ mA_p$

13-2   **a.** 0 A **b.** cosine wave, $I_{p\,C} = 2\pi \times 10\ Hz \times 1\ nF \times 6\ V_p = 377\ \mu A_p$

c. square wave, $i_{p\,C} = 1\ nF \times \left[\dfrac{6\ V}{25\ \mu s}\right] = 240\ \mu A_p$

13-3   **a.** $X_C = \dfrac{1}{2\pi \times 0\ Hz \times 100\ \mu F} = \infty\ \Omega,\ X_C = \dfrac{1}{2\pi \times 10\ Hz \times 100\ \mu F} = 159\ \Omega,$

$X_C = \dfrac{1}{2\pi \times 100\ Hz \times 100\ \mu F} = 15.9\ \Omega,\ X_C = \dfrac{1}{2\pi \times 1\ kHz \times 100\ \mu F} = 1.59\ \Omega,$

$$X_C = \frac{1}{2\pi \times 10 \text{ kHz} \times 100 \text{ }\mu F} = 0.16 \text{ }\Omega, \ X_C = \frac{1}{2\pi \times 100 \text{ kHz} \times 100 \text{ }\mu F} = 0.016 \text{ }\Omega,$$

b. open, **c.** short

13-4 **a.** $X_C = \frac{1}{2\pi \times 0 \text{ Hz} \times 0.1 \text{ }\mu F} = \infty \text{ }\Omega, \ X_C = \frac{1}{2\pi \times 10 \text{ Hz} \times 0.1 \text{ }\mu F} = 159 \text{ k }\Omega,$

$$X_C = \frac{1}{2\pi \times 100 \text{ Hz} \times 0.1 \text{ }\mu F} = 15.9 \text{ k }\Omega, \ X_C = \frac{1}{2\pi \times 1 \text{ kHz} \times 0.1 \text{ }\mu F} = 1.59 \text{ k }\Omega,$$

$$X_C = \frac{1}{2\pi \times 10 \text{ kHz} \times 0.1 \text{ }\mu F} = 159 \text{ }\Omega, \ X_C = \frac{1}{2\pi \times 100 \text{ kHz} \times 0.1 \text{ }\mu F} = 15.9 \text{ }\Omega$$

b. open, **c.** short

13-5 $f\uparrow \ X_C\downarrow \ v_C\downarrow \ v_R\uparrow \ i_R\uparrow \ i_C\uparrow$

13-6 $f\downarrow \ X_C\uparrow \ v_C\uparrow \ v_R\downarrow \ i_R\downarrow \ i_C\downarrow$

13-7 **a.** $X_C = \frac{1}{20\pi(0.1 \text{ }\mu F)} = 159 \text{ k }\Omega,$ open, $V_{out} = e_{supply} = 2 \text{ V}_{rms}$

b. $X_C = \frac{1}{2\pi(1 \text{ MHz}) \times 0.1 \text{ }\mu F} = 1.59 \text{ }\Omega,$ short, $V_{out} = e_{supply} - V_R = 0 \text{ V}_{rms}$

13-8 **a.** $X_C = \frac{1}{2\pi(10 \text{ MHz}) \times 0.1 \text{ }\mu F} = 159 \text{ k }\Omega,$ open, 0 V_{rms}

b. $X_C = \frac{1}{2\pi(1 \text{ MHz}) \times 0.1 \text{ }\mu F} = 1.59 \text{ }\Omega,$ short, $V_{out} = e_{supply} = 2 \text{ V}_{rms}$

13-9 $C_{total} = \frac{100 \text{ }\mu F}{3} 33.33 \text{ }\mu F$

13-10 $C_{total} = \left((100 \text{ }\mu F)^{-1} + (47 \text{ }\mu F)^{-1} + (33 \text{ }\mu F)^{-1}\right)^{-1} = 16.24 \text{ }\mu F$

13-11 $C_{total} = 3 \times 100 \text{ }\mu F = 300 \text{ }\mu F$

13-12 $C_{total} = 100 \text{ }\mu F + 47 \text{ }\mu F + 33 \text{ }\mu F = 180 \text{ }\mu F$

13-13   **a.** $Q_{total} = \left((100 \ \mu F)^{-1} + (47 \ \mu F)^{-1} + (33 \ \mu F)^{-1}\right)^{-1} \times 10 \ V = 162.4 \ \mu C$,   **b.** $162.4 \ \mu C$ each,

   c. $V_{C1} = \dfrac{162.4 \ \mu C}{100 \ \mu F} = 1.624 \ V$, $V_{C2} = \dfrac{162.4 \ \mu C}{47 \ \mu F} = 3.455 \ V$, $V_{C3} = \dfrac{162.4 \ \mu C}{33 \ \mu F} = 4.921 \ V$

   note: capacitor voltages in series add

13-14   **a.** $Q_{supplied} = 180 \ \mu F \times 10 \ V = 1800 \ \mu C$,   **b.** $V_{C1} = V_{C2} = V_{C3} = V_T = 10 \ V$,

   c. $Q_1 = 100 \ \mu F \times 10 \ V = 1000 \ \mu C$, $Q_2 = 47 \ \mu F \times 10 \ V = 470 \ \mu C$, $Q_3 = 33 \ \mu F \times 10 \ V = 330 \ \mu C$

13-15   **a.** capacitor open,   **b.** $0 \ V_{dc}$,   **c.** $V_C = e_{supply} = 6 \ V_{dc}$,   **d.** capacitor short,   **e.** $V_{RL} = 1 \ V_{rms}$,

   f. $V_C = 0 \ V_{rms}$,   **g.** ac output

13-16   **a.** capacitor open   **b.** $V_{RL} = 6 \ V_{dc} \times \dfrac{5 \ k\Omega}{1 \ k\Omega + 5 k\Omega} = 5 \ V_{dc}$ **c.** $V_C = V_{RL} = 5 \ V_{dc}$,

   d. capacitor short,   **e.** $V_{RL} = 0 \ V_{rms}$,   **f.** $V_C = 0 \ V_{rms}$,   **g.** dc output

13-17   **a.** $V_{base} = 30 \ V \times \dfrac{3.3 \ k\Omega}{3.3 \ k\Omega + 6.8 \ k\Omega} = 9.8 \ V_{dc}$, $V_{emitter} = 9.8 \ V_{dc} - 0.7 \ V = 9.1 \ V_{dc}$,

   $V_{collector} = 30 \ V - 13.2 \ V_{dc} = 16.8 \ V_{dc}$,   **b.** $9.8 \ V_{dc}$, 1 V_{pp} sine wave,   **c.** gain 1.45,

   $V_{collector} = \dfrac{6.8 \ k\Omega}{4.7 \ k\Omega} \times 1 \ V_{pp} = 1.45 \ V_{pp}$,   **d.** $16.8 \ V_{dc}$, 1.45 V_{pp} inverted sine wave,

   e. $0 \ V_{dc}$, 1.45 V_{pp} sine wave,   **f.** couple ac signals through (short to ac), block dc (open to dc)

13-18   **a.** capacitors open,   **b.** $6 \ V_{dc}$,   **c.** capacitor short,   **d.** $V_{pp \ op \ amp \ out} = 3.14 \times 1 \ V_{pp} = 3.14 \ V_{pp}$,   **e.** sine

   wave, $1.57 \ V_{max}$, $-1.57 \ V_{min}$, T of 1 ms,   **f.** sine wave, $7.57 \ V_{max}$, $4.43 \ V_{min}$, $6 \ V_{dc}$, T of 1 ms

Chapter 14

14-1   **a.** $\tau = 1 \ k\Omega \times 1 \ \mu F = 1 \ ms$,   **b.** $V_{C \ init} = \dfrac{0 \ C}{1 \ \mu F} = 0 \ V$, 20 mA with C *modeled* as a *short*,

   c. $V_{C \ ss} = 20 \ V$, $I_{C \ ss} = 0 \ mA$ with C *modeled* as an *open*,

   d. $V_C(t) = 20 \ V + (0 - 20) \ V \times e^{-t/1 \ ms} = 20 \ V - 20 \ V \cdot e^{-t/1 \ ms}$,

   $i_C(t) = 0 \ mA + (20 \ mA - 0 \ mA) \times e^{-t/1 \ ms} = 20 \ mA \cdot e^{-t/1 \ ms}$,

e. $V_C(2\tau) = 20\ \text{V} - 20\ \text{V} \times e^{-2\ \text{ms/1 ms}} = 17.3\ \text{V}$, $i_C(2\tau) = 20\ \text{mA} \times e^{-2\ \text{ms/1 ms}} = 2.71\ \text{mA}$,

f. exponential rise 0 V to 20 V in 5 ms, exponential fall 20 mA to 0 mA in 5 ms

14-2   **a.** $\tau = 1\ \text{k}\Omega \times 1\ \mu\text{F} = 1\ \text{ms}$, **b.** $V_{R\ \text{inuit}} = 20\ \text{V}$, $I_{R\ \text{init}} = \dfrac{20\ V_{dc}}{1\ \text{k}\Omega} = 20\ \text{mA}$ with C *modeled* as a *short*,

c. $V_{R\ ss} = 0\ \text{V}$, $I_{R\ ss} = 0\ \text{mA}$ with C *modeled* as an *open*,

d. $V_R(t) = 0\ \text{V} + (20\ \text{V} - 0\ \text{V}) \times e^{-t/1\ \text{ms}} = 20\ \text{V} \cdot e^{-t/1\ \text{ms}}$,

$i_R(t) = 0\ \text{mA} + (20\ \text{mA} - 0\ \text{mA}) \times e^{-t/1\ \text{ms}} = 20\ \text{mA} \cdot e^{-t/1\ \text{ms}}$,

e. $V_R(2\tau) = 20\ \text{V} \times e^{-2} = 2.71\ \text{V}$, $i_R(2\tau) = 20\ \text{mA} \times e^{-2} = 2.71\ \text{mA}$, **f.** exponential fall 20 V to 0 V in 5 ms, exponential fall 20 mA to 0 mA in 5 ms

14-3   **a.** $\tau = 1\ \text{k}\Omega \times 1\ \mu\text{F} = 1\ \text{ms}$, **b.** $V_{C\ \text{init}} = 8\ \text{V}$, $I_{C\ \text{init}} = \dfrac{20\ \text{V} - 8\ \text{V}}{1\ \text{k}\Omega} = 12\ \text{mA}$ with C *modeled* as sup-

ply E of 8 V, **c.** $V_{C\ ss} = 20\ \text{V}$, $I_{C\ ss} = 0\ \text{mA}$ with C *modeled* as an *open*,

d. $V_C(t) = 20\ \text{V} + (8\ \text{V} - 20\ \text{V}) \times e^{-t/1\ \text{ms}} = 20\ \text{V} - 12\ \text{V} \cdot e^{-t/1\ \text{ms}}$,

$i_C(t) = 0\ \text{mA} + (12\ \text{mA} - 0\ \text{mA}) \times e^{-t/1\ \text{ms}} = 12\ \text{mA} \cdot e^{-t/1\ \text{ms}}$,

e. $V_C(2\ \text{ms}) = (20\ \text{V} - 12\ \text{V}) \times e^{-2\ \text{ms/1 ms}} = 18.4\ \text{V}$, $i_C(2\ \text{ms}) = 12\ \text{mA} \times e^{-2\ \text{ms/1 ms}} = 1.62\ \text{mA}$,

f. exponential rise 8 V to 20 V in 5 ms, exponential fall 12 mA to 0 mA in 5 ms

14-4   **a.** $\tau = 1\ \text{k}\Omega \times 1\ \mu\text{F} = 1\ \text{ms}$, **b.** $V_{R\ \text{init}} = 20\ \text{V} - 8\ \text{V} = 12\ \text{V}$, $I_{R\ \text{init}} = \dfrac{12\ \text{V}}{1\ \text{k}\Omega} = 12\ \text{mA}$ with C *mod-*

eled as *supply* E of 8 V, **c.** $V_{R\ ss} = 0\ \text{V}$, $I_{R\ ss} = 0\ \text{mA}$ with C *modeled* as an *open*,

d. $V_R(t) = 0\ \text{V} + (12\ \text{V} - 0\ \text{V}) \times e^{-t/1\ \text{ms}} = 12\ \text{V} \cdot e^{-t/1\ \text{ms}}$,

$i_R(t) = 0\ \text{mA} + (12\ \text{mA} - 0\ \text{mA}) \times e^{-t/1\ \text{ms}} = 12\ \text{mA} \cdot e^{-t/1\ \text{ms}}$, **e.** $V_R(2\tau) = 12\ \text{V} \times e^{-2} = 1.62\ \text{V}$,

$i_R(2\tau) = 12\ \text{mA} \times e^{-2} = 1.62\ \text{mA}$, **f.** exponential fall 12 V to 0 V in 5 ms, exponential fall 12 mA to 0 mA in 5 ms

14-5   **a.** $V_{C\ \text{init}} = 20\ \text{V}$, **b.** $\tau = (1\ \text{k}\Omega + 1\ \text{k}\Omega) \times 1\ \mu\text{F} = 2\ \text{ms}$, **c.** $V_{C\ \text{init}} = 20\ \text{V}$,

$I_{C\ \text{init}} = \dfrac{-20\ \text{V}}{1\ \text{k}\Omega + 1\ \text{k}\Omega} = -10\ \text{mA}$ (direction opposite reference) with C *modeled* as E of 20 V,

d. $V_{C\,ss} = 0$ V, $I_{C\,ss} = 0$ mA, **e.** $V_C(t) = 0$ V $+ (20$ V $- 0$ V$)\times e^{-t/2\text{ ms}} = 20$ V$\cdot e^{-t/2\text{ ms}}$,

$i_C(t) = 0$ mA $+ (-10$ mA $- 0$ mA$)\times e^{-t/2\text{ ms}} = -10$ mA$\cdot e^{-t/2\text{ ms}}$,

f. $V_C(4$ ms$) = 20$ V$\times e^{-4\text{ ms}/2\text{ ms}} = 2.71$ V, $i_C(4$ ms$) = -10$ mA$\times e^{-4\text{ ms}/2\text{ ms}} = -1.35$ mA,

g. exponential fall 20 V to 0 V in 10 ms, exponential rise -10 mA to 0 mA in 10 ms

14-6   **a.** $V_{R\,init} = 0$ V, **b.** $\tau = (1$ k$\Omega + 1$ k$\Omega)\times 1$ μF $= 2$ ms, **c.** $V_{R\,init} = 20$ V$\times \dfrac{1\text{ k}\Omega}{2\text{ k}\Omega} = 10$ V,

$I_{R\,init} = \dfrac{10\text{ V}}{1\text{ k}\Omega} = 10$ mA, **d.** $V_{R\,ss} = 0$ V, $I_{R\,ss} = 0$ mA,

e. $V_R(t) = 0$ V $+ (10 - 0$ V$)\times e^{-t/2\text{ ms}} = 10$ V$\cdot e^{-t/2\text{ ms}}$,

$i_R(t) = 0$ mA $+ (-10$ mA $- 0$ mA$)\times e^{-t/2\text{ ms}} = 10$ mA$\cdot e^{-t/2\text{ ms}}$, **f.** $V_R(2\tau) = 10$ V$\times e^{-2} = 1.35$ V,

$i_R(2\tau) = 10$ mA$\times e^{-2} = 1.35$ mA, **g.** exponential fall 10 V to 0 V in 10 ms, exponential fall 10 V to 0 V in 10 ms

14-7   **a.** $\tau = 1$ k$\Omega \times 4.7$ μF $= 4.7$ ms, **b.** $V_C(t) = 12$ V $+ (0$ V $- 12$ V$)\times e^{-t/4.7\text{ ms}} = 12$ V $- 12$ V$\cdot e^{-t/4.7\text{ ms}}$,

c. $V_C(\tau) = 12$ V $- 12$ V$\times e^{-1} = 7.59$ V, $V_C(2\tau) = 12$ V $- 12$ V$\times e^{-2} = 10.4$ V,

$V_C(3\tau) = 12$ V $- 12$ V$\times e^{-3} = 11.4$ V, $V_C(4\tau) = 12$ V $- 12$ V$\times e^{-4} = 11.8$ V,

$V_C(5\tau) = 12$ V $- 12$ V$\times e^{-5} = 11.9$ V, **d.** $V_C(6$ ms$) = 12$ V $- 12$ V$\times e^{-6\text{ ms}/4.7\text{ ms}} = 8.65$ V,

e. $t = -4.7$ ms$\times \ln\left(\dfrac{9\text{ V} - 12\text{ V}}{-12\text{ V}}\right) = 6.52$ ms, **f.** exponential rise 0 V to 12 V in 23.5 ms and

stays at 12 V

14-8   **a.** $\tau = 100$ $\Omega \times 10$ μF $= 1$ ms, **b.** $V_C(t) = 8$ V $+ ((-4$ V$) + (-8$ V$))\times e^{-t/1\text{ ms}} = 8$ V $- 12$ V$\cdot e^{-t/1\text{ ms}}$,

c. $V_C(\tau) = 8$ V $- 12$ V$\times e^{-1} = 3.59$ V, $V_C(2\tau) = 8$ V $- 12$ V$\times e^{-2} = 6.38$ V,

$V_C(3\tau) = 8$ V $- 12$ V$\times e^{-3} = 7.40$ V, $V_C(4\tau) = 8$ V $- 12$ V$\times e^{-4} = 7.78$ V,

$V_C(5\tau) = 8$ V $- 12$ V$\times e^{-5} = 7.92$ V, **d.** $V_C(1.5$ ms$) = 8$ V $- 12$ V$\times e^{-1.5\text{ ms}/1\text{ ms}} = 5.32$ V,

e. $t = -1$ ms$\times \ln\left(\dfrac{6\text{ V} - 8\text{ V}}{-12\text{ V}}\right) = 1.79$ ms, **f.** exponential rise -4 V to 8 V in 5 ms and stays at 8 V

14-9   **a.** $\tau = 10$ k$\Omega \times 0.1$ μF $= 1$ ms, **b.** $i_C(t) = 0$ mA $+ (6$ mA $- 0$ mA$)\times e^{-t/1\text{ ms}} = 6$ mA$\cdot e^{-t/1\text{ ms}}$,

c. $I_C(\tau) = 6\text{ mA} \times e^{-1} = 2.21\text{ mA}$, $I_C(2\tau) = 6\text{ mA} \times e^{-2} = 812\ \mu\text{A}$, $I_C(3\tau) = 6\text{ mA} \times e^{-3} = 299\ \mu\text{A}$, $I_C(4\tau) = 6\text{ mA} \times e^{-4} = 110\ \mu\text{A}$, $I_C(5\tau) = 6\text{ mA} \times e^{-5} = 40\ \mu\text{A}$,

d. $i_C(500\ \mu\text{s}) = 6\text{ mA} \times e^{-500\ \mu\text{s/1 ms}} = 3.64\text{ mA}$, **e.** $t = -1\text{ ms} \times \ln\left(\dfrac{1\text{ mA}}{6\text{ mA}}\right) = 1.79\text{ ms}$,

f. exponential fall 6 mA to 0 mA in 5 ms and stays at 0 mA

14-10 **a.** $\tau = 100\text{ k}\Omega \times 0.01\ \mu\text{F} = 1\text{ ms}$, **b.** $V_C(t) = 0\text{ V} + (10\text{ V} - 0\text{ V}) \times e^{-t/1\text{ ms}} = 10\text{ V} \cdot e^{-t/1\text{ ms}}$,

c. $V_C(\tau) = 10\text{ V} \times e^{-1} = 3.68\text{ V}$, $V_C(2\tau) = 10\text{ V} \times e^{-2} = 1.35\text{ V}$, $V_C(3\tau) = 10\text{ V} \times e^{-3} = 498\text{ mV}$, $V_C(4\tau) = 10\text{ V} \times e^{-4} = 103\text{ mV}$, $V_C(5\tau) = 10\text{ V} \times e^{-5} = 67\text{ mV}$,

d. $V_C(2.5\text{ ms}) = 10\text{ V} \times e^{-2.5\text{ ms/1 ms}} = 821\text{ mV}$, **e.** $t = -1\text{ ms} \times \ln\left(\dfrac{9\text{ V}}{10\text{ V}}\right) = 105\ \mu\text{s}$, **f.** exponential fall 10 V to 0 V in 5 ms and stays at 0 V

14-11 **a.** $\tau = 2.2\text{ k}\Omega \times 1\ \mu\text{F} = 2.2\text{ ms}$, **b.** $T \geq 10\tau$? $T = \dfrac{1}{20\text{ Hz}} = 50\text{ ms} > 22\text{ ms}$? yes,

c. 0-25 ms exponential rise

   −4 V to +4 V in 11 ms

   25-50 ms exponential fall

   +4 V to −4 V in 11 ms,

d. 0-25 ms exponential fall

   +8 V to 0 V in 11 ms

   25-50 ms exponential rise

   −8 V to 0 V in 11 ms,

e. Use Ohm's Law: $i_R(t) = v_R(t) / R$,

   0-25 ms exponential fall

   +3.64 mA to 0 mA in 11 ms

   25-50 ms exponential rise

   −3.64 mA to 0 mA in 11 ms,

f. $t = -2.2\text{ ms} \times \ln\left(\dfrac{2\text{ V} - 4\text{ V}}{-8\text{ V}}\right) = 3.05\text{ ms}$

14-12   **a.** $\tau = 1\ k\Omega \times 1\ \mu F = 1\ ms$ **b.** $T \geq 10\tau$? $T = \dfrac{1}{100\ Hz} = 10\ ms \geq 10\ ms$? yes.

   c. 0-5 ms exponential rise

       0 V to 5 V in 5 ms
       5-10 ms exponential fall
         5 V to 0 V in 5 ms
   d. 0-5 ms exponential fall
       +5 V to 0 V in 5 ms
       5-10 ms exponential rise
       −5 V to 0 V in 5 ms
   e. Use Ohm's Law: $i_R(t) = v_R(t) / R$
       0-5 ms exponential fall
       +5 mA to 0 mA in 5 ms
       5-10 ms exponential rise
       −5 mA to 0 mA in 5 ms

   f. $t = -1\ ms \times \ln\left(\dfrac{0.8\ V}{5\ V}\right) = 1.83\ ms$

14-13 $t_r = 5.065\ ms - 232\ \mu s = 4.83\ ms$, $t_f = t_r = 4.83\ ms$

14-14 $t_r = 2.3\ ms - 105\ \mu s = 2.20\ ms$, $t_f = t_r = 2.20\ ms$

Chapter 15

15-1 $T = 1\ \mu s + 9\ \mu s = 10\ \mu s$, $W = 1\ \mu s$, $D = \dfrac{1\ \mu s}{10\ \mu s} \times 100\% = 10\%$, $f = \dfrac{1}{10\ \mu s} = 100\ kHz$

15-2 $T = \dfrac{1}{100\ pulses/sec} = 10\ ms$, $D = \dfrac{3\ ms}{10\ ms} \times 100\% = 30\%$

15-3 $W = t = -10\ ms \times \ln\left(\dfrac{3.33\ V - 5\ V}{-5\ V}\right) = 11\ ms$

15-4 $W = t_{\text{H}} = \ln\left(\dfrac{3.33\text{ V} - 5\text{ V}}{-3.33\text{ V}}\right) = 13.86\text{ ms}, \quad t_{\text{L}} = \ln\left(\dfrac{1.67\text{ V}}{3.33\text{ V}}\right) \times -10\text{ ms} = 6.93\text{ ms},$

$T = 13.86\text{ ms} + 6.93\text{ ms} = 20.79\text{ ms}, \quad D = \dfrac{13.86\text{ ms}}{20.79\text{ ms}} \times 100\% = 6.7\text{ \%},$

$f = \dfrac{1}{20.79\text{ μs}} = 48.1\text{ Hz}$

15-5 $W = t_{\text{H}} = \ln\left(\dfrac{3.33\text{ V} - 5\text{ V}}{-3.33\text{ V}}\right) = 13.86\text{ ms}, \quad t_{\text{L}} = \ln\left(\dfrac{1.67\text{ V}}{3.33\text{ V}}\right) \times -10\text{ ms} = 6.93\text{ ms},$

$T = 13.86\text{ ms} + 6.93\text{ ms} = 20.79\text{ ms}, \quad D = \dfrac{13.86\text{ ms}}{20.79\text{ ms}} \times 100\% = 6.7\text{ \%},$

$f = \dfrac{1}{20.79\text{ μs}} = 48.1\text{ Hz}$

15-6   **a.** yes, **b.** input R, feedback C, **c.** 1 MΩ **d.** ramp 0 V to -1 mV in 100 μs, **e.** inverted triangle wave, 5 mV$_{\text{p}}$, 10 kHz

15-7   **a.** yes, **b.** input R, feedback, C **c.** 100 kΩ **d.** ramp 0 V to -10 mV in 100 μs, **e.** inverted triangle wave, 50 mV$_{\text{p}}$, 10 kHz

15-8   **a.** yes, **b.** input C, feedback R, **c.** inverted spikes based on leading and lagging square wave edges and hitting rails of ±13 V, **d.** inverted square wave, 0.4 V$_{\text{p}}$, 10 Hz

15-9   **a.** yes, **b.** input C, feedback R, **c.** inverted spikes based on leading and lagging square wave edges and hitting rails of ±13 V, **d.** inverted square wave, 40 mV$_{\text{p}}$, 10 Hz

15-10   the original input signal if the rails are not reached

15-11   the original input signal if the rails are not reached

15-12   **a.** R$_{\text{i}}$, R$_{\text{f,}}$ **b.** R, C, **c.** $B = \dfrac{1\text{ kΩ}}{1\text{ kΩ} + 3.9\text{ kΩ}} = 0.204$, **d.** $V_{\text{UTP \& LTP}} = 0.2041 \times \pm10\text{ V} = \pm2.04\text{ V}$,

e. $T = 2 \times 413\text{ μs} = 828\text{ μs}, \quad f = \dfrac{1}{828\text{ μs}} = 1.21\text{ kHz}$ **f.** square wave,

10 V$_{\text{p}}$; square wave, 2.04 V$_{\text{p}}$; exponential wave, 2.04 V$_{\text{p}}$

15-13 $f_{\text{stage}-2} = \dfrac{1}{364\text{ μs}} = 2.74\text{ kHz}$

15-14 a. relaxation oscillator, **b.** square wave, **c.** $V_{p\ out\_1} = 13\ V_p$, $f_{stage\_1} = \dfrac{1}{828\ \mu s} = 1.21$ kHz,

d. integrator circuit, **e.** inverted triangle wave, **f.** $V_{P\ out\_2} = \dfrac{-(-13)\ V}{10\ k\Omega \times 10\ \mu F} \times 413\ \mu s = 54\ mV_p$,

$f_{stage\_2} = \dfrac{1}{828\ \mu s} = 1.21$ kHz

15-15 a. reduce R, C, or B (i.e., reduce R_i or raise R_f) **b.** decrease R2, decrease C2

15-16 a. $X_C = \dfrac{1}{2\pi \times 15\ Hz \times 0.1\ \mu F} = 106\ k\Omega$, **b.** $X_C = \dfrac{1}{2\pi \times 15\ Hz \times 0.01\ \mu F} = 106\ \Omega$,

c. $f_{half-power} = \dfrac{1}{2\pi \times 0.1\ \mu F \times 47.62\ \Omega} = 33.4$ kHz,

d. $\tau = 47.62\ \Omega \times 0.1\ \mu F = 4.76\ \mu s$, **e.** $5\ \tau = 23.8\ \mu s$, **f.** $2.2\ \tau = 10.5\ \mu s$

15-17 $C = \dfrac{1}{2\pi \times 15\ kHz \times 47.62\ \Omega} = 223$ nF

15-18 a. $X_C = \dfrac{1}{2\pi \times 1\ kHz \times 0.01\ nF} = 15.9\ M\Omega$, **b.** $X_C = \dfrac{1}{2\pi \times 10\ kHz \times 0.01\ nF} = 1.59\ M\Omega$,

c. $f_{half-power} = \dfrac{1}{2\pi \times 10\ M\Omega \times 0.01\ nF} = 1.59$ kHz, 1 kHz okay, 10 kHz erroneous measurement

d. $\tau = 10\ M\Omega \times 0.01\ nF = 100\ \mu s$ **e.** $5\ \tau = 500\ \mu s$ **f.** $2.2\ \tau = 220\ \mu s$

15-19 a. $V_{charged} = \dfrac{10\ M\Omega}{100\ k\Omega + 10\ M\Omega} \times 10\ V = 9.90\ V$, $\tau = 99\ k\Omega \times 100\ \mu F = 9.9\ s$, $5\ \tau = 49.5\ s$,

$2.2\ \tau = 21.8\ s$, **b.** $C = 10\ M\Omega \times 100\ \mu F = 1000\ s$, $5\ \tau = 5000\ s$, $2.2\ \tau = 2200\ s$

15-20 a. $V_{charged} = \dfrac{10\ M\Omega}{1\ k\Omega + 10\ M\Omega} \times 10\ V = 10.0\ V$, $\tau = 999\ \Omega \times 100\ \mu F = 100\ ms$, $5\ \tau = 500\ ms$,

$2.2\ \tau = 220\ ms$, **b.** $C = 10\ M\Omega \times 100\ \mu F = 1000\ s$, $5\ \tau = 5000\ s$, $2.2\ \tau = 2200\ s$

15-21 a. positive clipper, **b.** $0\ V_p$, $V_{out} = \dfrac{10\ k\Omega}{11\ k\Omega} \times (-5\ V_p) = -4.55\ V_{min}$, **c.** $0.2\ V_p$, $-4.55\ V_{min}$,

d. 0.7 V$_p$, -4.55 V$_{min}$, **e.** $I = \dfrac{5\ \text{V}_p - 0.7\ \text{V}}{1\ \text{k}\Omega} = 4.3\ \text{mA}_p$, **f.** 70 µA$_p$, -455 µA$_{min}$,

g. $V_{\text{diode reverse}} = V_{\text{load}} = 4.55\ \text{V}$

15-22   **a.** negative clipper, **b.** 0 V$_{min}$, $V_{out} = \dfrac{10\ \text{k}\Omega}{11\ \text{k}\Omega} \times 5\ \text{V}_p = 4.55\ \text{V}_p$ **c.** -0.2 V$_{min}$, 4.55 V$_p$,

d. -0.7 V$_{min}$, 4.55 V$_p$, **e.** $I = \dfrac{5\ \text{V}_p - 0.7\ \text{V}}{1\ \text{k}\Omega} = 4.3\ \text{mA}_p$, **f.** -70 µA$_{min}$, 455 mA$_p$,

g. $V_{\text{diode reverse}} = V_{\text{load}} = 4.55\ \text{V}$

15-23   **a.** rectifier circuit, positive half wave signal out, **b.** 5.0 V$_p$, 0 V$_{min}$, **c.** 4.8 V$_p$, 0 V$_{min}$,

d. 4.3 V$_p$, 0 V$_{min}$, **e.** $I = \dfrac{4.3\ \text{V}_p}{1\ \text{k}\Omega} = 4.3\ \text{mA}_p$, **f.** positive half wave, 4.3 mA$_p$, 0 V$_{min}$,

g. $V_{\text{diode reverse}} = 5\ \text{V}$

15-24   **a.** input capacitor filtered rectifier, positive dc output with an ac ripple voltage
b. $\sim$ 5 V$_{dc}$ **c.** $\sim$ 4.8 V$_{dc}$ **d.** $\sim$ 4.3 V$_{dc}$

15-25 -4 V$_{dc}$

Chapter 16

16-1   **a.** 0 A, **b.** cosine wave, $V_{p\,L} = 2\pi \times 100\ \text{Hz} \times 1\ \text{µH} = 628\ \text{µV}_p$

c. square wave, $V_{p\,L} = 1\ \text{µH} \times \dfrac{10\ \text{A}_p}{2.5\ \text{ms}} = 4\ \text{mV}_p$

16-2   **a.** 0 A **b.** cosine wave, $V_{p\,L} = 2\pi \times 10\ \text{kHz} \times 1\ \text{nH} \times 6\ \text{A}_p = 377\ \text{µV}_p$

c. square wave, $V_{p\,L} = 1\ \text{nH} \times \dfrac{6\ \text{A}_p}{25\ \text{µs}} = 240\ \text{µV}_p$

16-3   **a.** $X_L = 2\pi \times 22\ \text{mH} \times 0\ \text{Hz} = 0\ \Omega$, $X_L = 2\pi \times 22\ \text{mH} \times 10\ \text{Hz} = 1.38\ \Omega$,
$X_L = 2\pi \times 22\ \text{mH} \times 100\ \text{Hz} = 13.8\ \Omega$, $X_L = 2\pi \times 22\ \text{mH} \times 1\ \text{kHz} = 138\ \Omega$,
$X_L = 2\pi \times 22\ \text{mH} \times 10\ \text{kHz} = 1.38\ \text{k}\Omega$, $X_L = 2\pi \times 22\ \text{mH} \times 100\ \text{kHz} = 13.8\ \text{k}\Omega$ **b.** short **c.**
open

16-4   **a.** $X_L = 2\pi \times 0.1 \text{ mH} \times 0 \text{ Hz} = 0 \text{ }\Omega$, $X_L = 2\pi \times 0.1 \text{ mH} \times 10 \text{ Hz} = 6.28 \text{ m}\Omega$,
$X_L = 2\pi \times 0.1 \text{ mH} \times 100 \text{ Hz} = 62.8 \text{ m}\Omega$, $X_L = 2\pi \times 0.1 \text{ mH} \times 1 \text{ kHz} = 628 \text{ m}\Omega$,
$X_L = 2\pi \times 0.1 \text{ mH} \times 10 \text{ kHz} = 6.28 \text{ }\Omega$, $X_L = 2\pi \times 0.1 \text{ mH} \times 100 \text{ kHz} = 62.8 \text{ }\Omega$ **b.** short

c. open

16-5   f ↑ X_L ↑ v_L ↑ v_R ↓ i_R ↓ i_L ↓

16-6   f ↓ X_L ↓ v_L ↓ v_R ↑ i_R ↑ i_L ↑

16-7   **a.** $X_L = 2\pi \times 2.2 \text{ mH} \times 1 \text{ Hz} = 13.8 \text{ m}\Omega$, short, 0 V_{rms},
b. $X_L = 2\pi \times 2.2 \text{ mH} \times 10 \text{ MHz} = 138 \text{ k}\Omega$, open, 2 V_{rms}

16-8   **a.** $X_L = 2\pi \times 1 \text{ mH} \times 1 \text{ Hz} = 6.28 \text{ m}\Omega$, short, 2 V_{rms},
b. $X_L = 2\pi \times 1 \text{ mH} \times 10 \text{ MHz} = 62.8 \text{ k}\Omega$, open, 0 V_{rms}

16-9   **a.** $L_T = 3 \times 3 \text{ mH} = 9 \text{ mH}$, **b.** $X_L = 2\pi \times 9 \text{ mH} \times 1 \text{ kHz} = 56.5 \text{ }\Omega$,

16-10   **a.** $L_T = \dfrac{L}{3} = 1 \text{ mH}$, **b.** $X_L = 2\pi \times 1 \text{ mH} \times 1 \text{ kHz} = 6.28 \text{ }\Omega$

16-11   **a.** $\tau = \dfrac{2 \text{ mH}}{1 \text{ k}\Omega} = 2 \text{ }\mu s$, **b.** $V_{L\text{ limit}} = 20 \text{ V}$, $i_{L\text{ limit}} = 0 \text{ mA}$ with L *modeled* as *open*,

c. $V_{L\text{ ss}} = 0 \text{ V}$, $i_{L\text{ ss}} = 20 \text{ mA}$ with L *modeled* as *short*,

d. $V_L(t) = 0 \text{ V} + (20 - 0) \text{ V} \times e^{-t/2 \text{ }\mu s} = 20 \text{ V} \cdot e^{-t/2 \text{ }\mu s}$,
$i_L(t) = 20 \text{ mA} + (0 \text{ mA} - 20 \text{ mA}) \times e^{-t/2 \text{ }\mu s} = 20 \text{ mA} - 20 \text{ mA} \cdot e^{-t/2 \text{ }\mu s}$,
e. $V_L(2\tau) = 20\text{V} \times e^{-2} = 2.71 \text{ V}$, $i_L(2\tau) = 20 \text{ mA} - 20 \text{ mA} \times e^{-2} = 17.3 \text{ mA}$,
f. spike 0 V to 20 V then exponential fall 20 V to 0 V in 10 μs, exponential rise from 0 mA to 20 mA in 10 μs

16-12   **a.** $\tau = \dfrac{2 \text{ mH}}{1 \text{ k}\Omega} = 2 \text{ }\mu s$, **b.** $V_R = 0 \text{ V}$, $i_R = 0 \text{ mA}$ with L *modeled* as *open*,

c. $V_R = e_{supply} = 20 \text{ V}$, $i_R = \dfrac{20 \text{ V}}{1 \text{ }\Omega k} = 20 \text{ mA}$ L *modeled* as *short*,

d. $V_R(t) = 20 \text{ V} - 20 \text{ V} \times e^{-t/2 \text{ }\mu s} = 20 \text{ V} - 20 \text{ V} \cdot e^{-t/2 \text{ }\mu s}$,
$i_R(t) = 20 \text{ mA} - 20 \text{ mA} \times e^{-t/2 \text{ }\mu s} = 20 \text{ mA} - 20 \text{ mA} \cdot e^{-t/2 \text{ }\mu s}$,
e. $V_R(2\tau) = 20 \text{ V} - 20\text{V} \times e^{-2} = 17.3 \text{ V}$, $i_R(2\tau) = 20 \text{ mA} - 20 \text{ mA} \times e^{-2} = 17.3 \text{ mA}$,

f. exponential rise 0 V to 20 V in 10 μs, exponential rise 0 mA to 20 mA in 10 μs

16-13 **a.** $\tau = \dfrac{2\ \text{mH}}{1\ \text{k}\Omega} = 2\ \mu\text{s}$ **b.** $V_{\text{L limit}} = 20\ \text{V} - (2\ \text{mA} \times 1\ \text{k}\Omega) = 18\ \text{V}$, $I_{\text{L limit}} = 2\ \text{mA}$ with L *modeled*

as *supply* I of 2 mA, **c.** 0 V, $I_{\text{L limit}} = \dfrac{20\ \text{V}}{1\ \text{k}\Omega} = 20\ \text{mA}$ with L *modeled* as a *short,*

d. $V_{\text{L}}(t) = 0\ \text{V} + (18 - 0)\text{V} \times e^{-t/2\ \mu\text{s}} = 18\ \text{V}\ e^{-t/2\mu\text{s}}$,

$i_{\text{L}}(t) = 20\ \text{mA} + (2\ \text{mA} - 20\ \text{mA}) \times e^{-t/2\ \mu\text{s}} = 20\ \text{mA} - 18\ \text{mA}\ e^{-t/2\mu\text{s}}$,

e. $V_{\text{L}}(3\ \mu\text{s}) = 18\ \text{V} \times e^{-3\ \mu\text{s}/2\ \mu\text{s}} = 4.02\ \text{V}$, $i_{\text{L}}(3\ \mu\text{s}) = 20\ \text{mA} - 18\ \text{mA} \times e^{-3\ \mu\text{s}/2\ \mu\text{s}} = 16.0\ \text{mA}$,

f. spike 0 V to 18 V then exponential fall 18 V to 0 V in 10 μs, exponential rise 2 mA to 20 mA in 10 μs

16-14 **a.** $\tau = \dfrac{2\ \text{mH}}{1\ \text{k}\Omega} = 2\ \mu\text{s}$, **b.** $V_{\text{R init}} = 2\ \text{V}$, $i_{\text{R init}} = 2\ \text{mA}$ with L *modeled* as *supply* I of 2 mA,

c. $V_{\text{R ss}} = 20\ \text{V}$, $i_{\text{R ss}} = 20\ \text{mA}$ with L *modeled* as a *short,*

d. $V_{\text{R}}(t) = 20\ \text{V} - 18\ \text{V} \times e^{-t/2\ \mu\text{s}} = 20\ \text{V} - 18\ \text{V}\ e^{-t/2\ \mu\text{s}}$,

$i_{\text{R}}(t) = 20\ \text{mA} - 18\ \text{mA} \times e^{-t/2\ \mu\text{s}} = 20\ \text{mA} - 18\ \text{mA}\ e^{-t/2\ \mu\text{s}}$,

e. $V_{\text{R}}(3\ \mu\text{s}) = 20\ \text{V} - 18\ \text{V} \times e^{-3\ \mu\text{s}/2\ \mu\text{s}} = 16.0\ \text{V}$,

$i_{\text{R}}(3\ \mu\text{s}) = 20\ \text{mA} - 18\ \text{mA} \times e^{-3\ \mu\text{s}/2\ \mu\text{s}} = 16.0\ \text{mA}$, **f.** exponential rise 2 V to 20 V in 10 μs, exponential rise 2 mA to 20 mA in 10 μs

16-15 **a.** $\tau = \dfrac{2.2\ \text{mH}}{1\ \text{k}\Omega} = 2.2\ \mu\text{s}$, **b.** $T \geq 10\tau$? $T = \dfrac{1}{20\ \text{kHz}} = 50\ \mu\text{s} > 22\ \mu\text{s}$? yes.

c. 0-25 μs exponential rise,

  −4 V to +4 V in 11 μs
  25-50 μs exponential fall
   +4 V to −4 V in 11 μs
d. Use Ohm's Law: $i_{\text{R}}(t) = v_{\text{R}}(t) / \text{R}$
  0-25 μs exponential rise
   −4 mA to +4 mA in 11μs
  25-50 μs exponential fall
   +4 mA to −4 mA in 11 μs
e. 0-25 μs spike to 8 V then exponential
  fall +8 V to 0 V in 11 μs

25-50 μs spike to −8 V then exponential rise −8 V to 0 V in 11 μs

f. $t = -2.2 \ \mu s \times \ln\left(\dfrac{1 \ mA - 4 \ mA}{-8 \ mA}\right) = 2.16 \ \mu s$

16-16 **a.** $\tau = \dfrac{1 \ mH}{1 \ k\Omega} = 1 \ \mu s$

b. $T \geq 10\tau$? $10 \ \mu s \geq 10 \ \mu s$? yes.
c. 0-5 μs exponential rise 0 V to 4 V
   5-10 μs exponential fall 4 V to 0 V
d. Use Ohm's Law: $i_R(t) = v_R(t) \ / \ R$
   0-5 μs exponential rise 0 mA to 4 mA
   5-10 μs exponential fall 4 mA to 0 mA
e. 0-5 μs spike to 4 V then
      exponential fall 4 V to 0 V in 5 μs
   5-10 μs spike to −4 V then
      exponential rise −4 V to 0 V in 5 μs

f. $t = \ln\left(2\dfrac{1 \ mA - 4 \ mA}{-4 \ mA}\right) \times -1 \ \mu s = 693 \ ns$

Chapter 17

17-1 **a.** $V_1 = e_{supply} = 108 \ V_{rms}$, **b.** $V_2 = \dfrac{108 \ V_{rms}}{3} = 36 \ V_{rms}$, **c.** $i_2 = \dfrac{36 \ V_{rms}}{4 \ k\Omega} = 9 \ mA_{rms}$,

d. $P_2 = 9 \ mA_{rms} \times 36 \ V_{rms} = 324 \ mW$, **e.** $P_1 = P_2 = 324 \ mW$, **f.** $i_1 = \dfrac{324 \ mW}{108 \ V_{rms}} = 3 \ mA_{rms}$,

g. $r_1 = \dfrac{108 \ V_{rms}}{3 \ mA_{rms}} = 36 \ k\Omega$

17-2 **a.** $r_1 = \left(\dfrac{3}{1}\right)^2 \times 4 \ k\Omega = 36 \ k\Omega$, **b.** $i_1 = \dfrac{108 \ V_{rms}}{36 \ k\Omega + 18 \ k\Omega} = 2 \ mA_{rms}$,

c. $V_1 = 2 \ mA_{rms} \times 36 \ k\Omega = 72 \ V_{rms}$, **d.** $V_2 = 72 \ V_{rms} \times \dfrac{1}{3} = 24 \ V_{rms}$,

e. $i_2 = \dfrac{2 \text{ mA}_{\text{rms}} \times 72 \text{ V}_{\text{rms}}}{24 \text{ V}_{\text{rms}}} = 6 \text{ mA}_{\text{rms}},$ **f.** $P_2 = 2 \text{ mA}_{\text{rms}} \times 72 \text{ V}_{\text{rms}} = 144 \text{ mW},$

g. $P_1 = 2 \text{ mA}_{\text{rms}} \times 72 \text{ V}_{\text{rms}} = 144 \text{ mW}$

17-3 **a.** $e_{\text{Th}} = 108 \text{ V}_{\text{rms}} \times \dfrac{1}{3} = 36 \text{ V}_{\text{rms}},$ **b.** $r_{\text{Th}} = \left(\dfrac{1}{3}\right)^2 \times 0 \text{ }\Omega = 0 \text{ }\Omega,$ **c.** $36 \text{ V}_{\text{rms}}$ with $0 \text{ }\Omega,$

d. $V_{\text{load}} = e_{\text{Th}} = 36 \text{ V}_{\text{rms}},$ **e.** $i_{\text{load}} = \dfrac{36 \text{ V}_{\text{rms}}}{4 \text{ k}\Omega} = 9 \text{ mA}_{\text{rms}}$

17-4 **a.** $e_{\text{Th}} = 108 \text{ V}_{\text{rms}} \times \dfrac{1}{3} = 36 \text{ V}_{\text{rms}},$ **b.** $r_{\text{Th}} = \left(\dfrac{1}{3}\right)^2 \times 18 \text{ k}\Omega = 2 \text{ k}\Omega,$

c. $36 \text{ V}_{\text{rms}}$ with series $2 \text{ k}\Omega,$ **d.** $V_{\text{load}} = e_{\text{Th}} = 36 \text{ V}_{\text{rms}} \times \dfrac{4 \text{ k}\Omega}{6 \text{ k}\Omega} = 24 \text{ V}_{\text{rms}},$

e. $i_{\text{load}} = \dfrac{24 \text{ V}_{\text{rms}}}{4 \text{ k}\Omega} = 6 \text{ mA}_{\text{rms}}$

17-5 **a.** $V_1 = e_{\text{supply}} = 108 \text{ V}_{\text{rms}},$ **b.** $V_2 = 108 \text{ V}_{\text{rms}} \times \dfrac{2}{1} = 216 \text{ V}_{\text{rms}},$

c. $i_2 = \dfrac{216 \text{ V}_{\text{rms}}}{4 \text{ k}\Omega} = 54 \text{ mA}_{\text{rms}},$ **d.** $P_2 = 54 \text{ mA}_{\text{rms}} \times 216 \text{ V}_{\text{rms}} = 11.66 \text{ W},$

e. $P_1 = 54 \text{ mA}_{\text{rms}} \times 216 \text{ V}_{\text{rms}} = 11.66 \text{ W}$ **f.** $i_1 = \dfrac{11.664 \text{ W}}{108 \text{ V}_{\text{rms}}} = 108 \text{ mA}_{\text{rms}},$

g. $r_1 = \dfrac{108 \text{ V}_{\text{rms}}}{108 \text{ mA}_{\text{rms}}} = 1 \text{ k}\Omega$

17-6 **a.** $r_1 = \left(\dfrac{1}{2}\right)^2 \times 4 \text{ k}\Omega = 1 \text{ k}\Omega,$ **b.** $i_1 = \dfrac{108 \text{ V}_{\text{rms}}}{1 \text{ k}\Omega + 18 \text{ k}\Omega} = 5.684 \text{ mA}_{\text{rms}},$

c. $V_1 = 5.684 \text{ mA}_{\text{rms}} \times 1 \text{ k}\Omega = 5.684 \text{ V}_{\text{rms}},$ **d.** $V_2 = 5.684 \text{ V}_{\text{rms}} \times \dfrac{2}{1} = 11.37 \text{ V}_{\text{rms}},$

e. $i_2 = 5.684 \text{ V}_{\text{rms}} \times \left(\dfrac{1}{2}\right) = 2.842 \text{ mA}_{\text{rms}},$ **f.** $P_2 = 5.684 \text{ mA}_{\text{rms}} \times 5.684 \text{ V}_{\text{rms}} = 32.31 \text{ mW},$

g. $P_1 = 5.684 \text{ mA}_{\text{rms}} \times 5.684 \text{ V}_{\text{rms}} = 32.31 \text{ mW}$

17-7   **a.** $e_{Th} = 108 \text{ V}_{rms} \times \dfrac{2}{1} = 216 \text{ V}_{rms}$,   **b.** $r_{Th} = \left(\dfrac{2}{1}\right)^2 \times 0 \text{ } \Omega = 0 \text{ } \Omega$,   **c.** 216 V_{rms} with $0 \text{ } \Omega$,

     d. $V_{load} = e_{Th} = 216 \text{ V}_{rms}$,   **e.** $i_L = \dfrac{216 \text{ V}_{rms}}{4 \text{ k}\Omega} = 54 \text{ mA}_{rms}$

17-8   **a.** $e_{Th} = 108 \text{ V}_{rms} \times \dfrac{2}{1} = 216 \text{ V}_{rms}$,   **b.** $r_{Th} = \left(\dfrac{2}{1}\right)^2 \times 18 \text{ k}\Omega = 72 \text{ k}\Omega$,

     c. 216 V_{rms} with series $72 \text{ k}\Omega$,

     d. $V_{load} = e_{Th} = 216 \text{ V}_{rms} \times \dfrac{4 \text{ k}\Omega}{4 \text{ k}\Omega + 72 \text{ k}\Omega} = 216 \text{ V}_{rms} \times \dfrac{4 \text{ k}\Omega}{76 \text{ k}\Omega} = 11.37 \text{ V}_{rms}$,

     e. $i_{load} = \dfrac{11.37 \text{ V}_{rms}}{4 \text{ k}\Omega} = 2.482 \text{ mA}_{rms}$

17-9   Thévenin model: 20 V_{rms}, $2 \text{ k}\Omega$; load: $V_{load} = 20 \text{ V}_{rms} \times \dfrac{18 \text{ k}\Omega}{20 \text{ k}\Omega} = 18 \text{ V}_{rms}$,

     $i_{load} = \dfrac{18 \text{ V}_{rms}}{18 \text{ k}\Omega} = 1 \text{ mA}_{rms}$

17-10 $V_{p\ load} = 15 \text{ V}_{rms} \times \sqrt{2} = 21.2 \text{ V}_p$, $V_{pp\ load} = 2\left(21.2 \text{ V}_p\right) = 42.4 \text{ V}_{pp}$

Chapter 18

18-1   **a.** $V_{p\ 2} = 120 \text{ V}_{rms} \times \dfrac{1}{10} = 17 \text{ V}_p$, $V_{p\ out} = 17.0 \text{ V}_p - 0.7 \text{ V} = 16.3 \text{ V}_p$, $I_{p\ load} = \dfrac{16.3 \text{ V}_p}{1 \text{ k}\Omega} = 32.6 \text{ mA}_p$,

     b. $f_{out} = f_{in} = 60 \text{ Hz}$, $T = \dfrac{1}{60 \text{ Hz}} = 16.7 \text{ ms}$,

     c. half-wave, 16.7 ms, 16.3 V_p; half-wave, 16.7 ms, 32.6 mA_p,

     d. $I_{ave\ load} = \dfrac{32.6 \text{ mA}}{\pi} = 10.4 \text{ mA}_{dc}$, $I_D = I_{ave\ load} = 10.4 \text{ mA}_{dc}$, diode safe ,

     e. $PIV = V_{p\ 2} = 17 \text{ V}_p$, diode does not break down

18-2   **a.** $V_{p\,2} = 120\ V_{rms} \times \dfrac{1}{10} = 17\ V_p$, $V_{p\ out} = 17.0\ V_p - 0.7\ V = 16.3\ V_p$, $I_{p\ load} = \dfrac{16.3\ V_p}{1\ k\Omega} = 16.3\ mA_p$,

     b. $f_{out} = f_{in} = 60\ Hz$, $T = \dfrac{1}{60\ Hz} = 16.7\ ms$,

     c. half-wave, 16.7 ms, 16.3 V_p; half-wave, 16.7 ms, 16.3 mA_p,

     d. 5.2 mA_{dc}, 5.2 mA_{dc}, diode safe,   **e.** $PIV = V_{p\,2} = 17\ V_p$, diode does not break down

18-3   **a.** $V_{p\,2} = 120\ V_{rms} \times \sqrt{2} \times \dfrac{1}{10} = 17\ V_p$, $V_{p\ out} = 17.0\ V_p - 0.7\ V = 16.3\ V_p$,

     $I_{p\ out} = \dfrac{16.3\ V_p}{500\ \Omega} = 32.6\ mA_p$,   **b.** $f_{out} = f_{in} = 60\ Hz$, $T = \dfrac{1}{60\ Hz} = 16.7\ ms$,

     c. $RC = 500\ \Omega \times 220\ \mu F = 16.7\ ms \ll 110\ ms$, $V_{pp} = 16.3\ V_p - 13.83\ V_{min} = 2.47\ V_{pp}$,

     $V_{rms} = \dfrac{2.47\ V_{pp}}{2 \times \sqrt{3}} = 713\ mV_{rms}$,

     d. $V_{min} = 16.3\ V_p \left(1 - \dfrac{16.67\ ms}{110\ ms}\right) = 13.83\ V_{min}$, $V_{dc} = \left(\dfrac{16.3\ V_p + 13.8\ V_{min}}{2}\right) = 15.0\ V_{dc}$

     e. triangle wave, 16.7 ms, 16.3 V_p, 13.8 V_{min},   **f.** $\% ripple = \dfrac{722\ mV_{rms}}{15.05\ V_{dc}} \times 100\ \% = 4.77\ \%$

     g. $PIV = 17.0\ V_p + 16.3\ V_p = 33.3\ V_p$, diode does not break down

18-4   **a.** $V_{p\,2} = 120\ V_{rms} \times \sqrt{2} \times \dfrac{1}{10} = 17\ V_p$, $V_{p\ out} = 17.0\ V_p - 0.7\ V = 16.3\ V_p$,

     $I_{p\,2} = \dfrac{16.3\ V_p}{1\ k\Omega} = 16.3\ mA_p$,   **b.** $f_{out} = f_{in} = 60\ Hz$, $T = \dfrac{1}{60\ Hz} = 16.7\ ms$,

     c. $RC = 1\ k\Omega \times 220\ \mu F = 16.7\ ms \ll 220\ ms$, $V_{pp} = \dfrac{16.3\ V_p}{1\ k\Omega \times 60\ Hz \times 220\ \mu F} = 1.24\ V_{pp}$,

     $V_{rms} = \dfrac{1.24\ V_{pp}}{2 \times \sqrt{3}} = 356\ mV_{rms}$,   **d.** $V_{min} = 16.3\ V_p - 1.24\ V_{pp} = 15.1\ V_{min}$,

     $V_{dc} = \dfrac{1}{2}\left(16.3\ V_p + 15.07\ V_{min}\right) = 15.7\ V_{dc}$,   **e.** triangle wave, 16.7 ms, 16.3 V_p, 15.1 V_{min},

f. $\% \ ripple = \dfrac{356 \ \text{mV}_{\text{rms}}}{15.68 \ \text{V}_{\text{dc}}} \times 100\% = 2.27\%$, **g.** $PIV = 17.0 \ \text{V}_\text{p} + 16.3 \ \text{V}_\text{p} = 33.3 \ \text{V}_\text{p}$, diode does not

break down

18-5 **a.** $V_{\text{p 2}} = 120 \ \text{V}_{\text{rms}} \times \sqrt{2} \times \dfrac{1}{10} = 17 \ \text{V}_\text{p}$, $V_{\text{p out}} = \dfrac{17.0 \ \text{V}_\text{p}}{2} - 0.7 \ \text{V} = 7.8 \ \text{V}_\text{p}$,

$I_{\text{p out}} = \dfrac{7.8 \ \text{V}_\text{p}}{500 \ \Omega} = 15.6 \ \text{mA}_\text{p}$, **b.** $f_{\text{out}} = 2 \times 60 \ \text{Hz} = 120 \ \text{Hz}$, $T = \dfrac{1}{120 \ \text{Hz}} = 8.33 \ \text{ms}$, **c.** full-wave,

8.33 ms, 7.8 V$_\text{p}$; full-wave, 8.33 ms, 15.6 mA$_\text{p}$, **d.** $I_{\text{dc load}} = \dfrac{2 \times 15.6 \ \text{mA}_\text{p}}{\pi} = 9.93 \ \text{mA}_{\text{dc}}$,

$I_{\text{dc diode}} = \dfrac{9.93 \ \text{mA}_{\text{dc}}}{2} = 4.97 \ \text{mA}_{\text{dc}}$, diode safe, **e.** $PIV = 17 \ \text{V}_{\text{p 2}} - 0.7 \ \text{V} = 16.3 \ \text{V}_\text{p}$, diode does not
break down

18-6 **a.** $V_{\text{p 2}} = 120 \ \text{V}_{\text{rms}} \times \sqrt{2} \times \dfrac{1}{10} = 17 \ \text{V}_\text{p}$, $V_{\text{p out}} = \dfrac{17.0 \ \text{V}_\text{p}}{2} - 0.7 \ \text{V} = 7.8 \ \text{V}_\text{p}$,

$I_{\text{p out}} = \dfrac{7.8 \ \text{V}_\text{p}}{1 \ \text{k}\Omega} = 7.8 \ \text{mA}_\text{p}$, **b.** $f_{\text{out}} = 2 \times 60 \ \text{Hz} = 120 \ \text{Hz}$, $T = \dfrac{1}{120 \ \text{Hz}} = 8.33 \ \text{ms}$, **c.** full-wave,

8.33 ms, 7.8 V$_\text{p}$; full-wave, 8.33 ms, 7.8 mA$_\text{p}$, **d.** $I_{\text{dc load}} = \dfrac{2 \times 7.8 \ \text{mA}_\text{p}}{\pi} = 4.97 \ \text{mA}_{\text{dc}}$,

$I_{\text{dc diode}} = \dfrac{4.97 \ \text{mA}_{\text{dc}}}{2} \ 2.48 \ \text{mA}_{\text{dc}}$, diode safe, **e.** $PIV = 17 \ \text{V}_{\text{p 2}} - 0.7 \ \text{V} = 16.3 \ \text{V}_\text{p}$, diode does not
break down

18-7 **a.** $V_{\text{p 2}} = 120 \ \text{V}_{\text{rms}} \times \sqrt{2} \times \dfrac{1}{10} = 17 \ \text{V}_\text{p}$, $V_{\text{p out}} = \dfrac{17.0 \ \text{V}_\text{p}}{2} - 0.7 \ \text{V} = 7.8 \ \text{V}_\text{p}$,

$I_{\text{p out}} = \dfrac{7.8 \ \text{V}_\text{p}}{500 \ \Omega} = 15.6 \ \text{mA}_\text{p}$, **b.** $f_{\text{out}} = 2 \times 60 \ \text{Hz} = 120 \ \text{Hz}$, $T = \dfrac{1}{120 \ \text{Hz}} = 8.33 \ \text{ms}$

c. 8.33 ms << 110 ms, 591 mV$_\text{pp}$, 171 mV$_\text{rms}$, **d.** $V_{\text{min}} = 7.8 \ \text{V}_\text{p}(1 - 0.07575) = 7.2 \ \text{V}_{\text{min}}$,

$V_{\text{dc}} = \left(\dfrac{7.8 \ \text{V}_\text{p} + 7.2 \ \text{V}_{\text{min}}}{2} \right) = 7.5 \ \text{V}_{\text{dc}}$, **e.** triangle wave, 8.33 ms, 7.8 V$_\text{p}$, 7.2 V$_{\text{min}}$,

f. $\% \ ripple = \dfrac{171 \ \text{mV}_{\text{rms}}}{7.5 \ \text{V}_{\text{dc}}} \times 100\% = 2.3 \ \%$, **g.** $PIV = 17.0 \ \text{V}_\text{p} - 0.7 \ \text{V}_\text{p} = 16.3 \ \text{V}_\text{p}$, diode does not

break down

18-8 **a.** $V_{p\,2} = 120\,V_{rms} \times \sqrt{2} \times \dfrac{1}{10} = 17\,V_p$, $V_{p\,out} = \dfrac{17.0\,V_p}{2} - 0.7\,V = 7.8\,V_p$,

$I_{p\,out} = \dfrac{7.8\,V_p}{500\,\Omega} = 7.8\,mA_p$, **b.** $f_{out} = 2 \times 120\,Hz = 120\,Hz$, $T = \dfrac{1}{120\,Hz} = 8.33\,ms$

c. 8.33 ms << 220 ms, 296 mV$_{pp}$, 86 mV$_{rms}$, **d.** $V_{min} = 7.8\,V_p - 296\,mV_{pp} = 7.5\,V_{min}$,

$V_{dc} = \left(\dfrac{7.8\,V_p + 7.5\,V_{min}}{2} \right) = 7.7\,V_{dc}$, **e.** triangle wave, 8.33 ms, 7.8 V$_p$, 7.5 V$_{min}$,

f. $\% \, ripple = \dfrac{86\,mV_{rms}}{7.65\,V_{dc}} \times 100\% = 1.1\,\%$ **g.** $PIV = 17.0\,V_p - 0.7\,V_p = 16.3\,V_p$, diode does not break down

18-9 **a.** $V_{p\,2} = 120\,V_{rms} \times \sqrt{2} \times \dfrac{1}{10} = 17\,V_p$, $V_{p\,out} = 17.0\,V_p - 1.4\,V = 15.6\,V_p$,

$I_{p\,out} = \dfrac{15.6\,V_p}{500\,\Omega} = 31.2\,mA_p$, **b.** $f_{out} = 2 \times 120\,Hz = 120\,Hz$, $T = \dfrac{1}{120\,Hz} = 8.33\,ms$,

c. full-wave, 8.33 ms, 15.6 V$_p$; full-wave, 8.33 ms, 31.2 mA$_p$,

d. $I_{dc\,load} = \dfrac{2 \times \left(\dfrac{15.6\,v_p}{\pi} \right)}{500\,\Omega} = 19.9\,mA_{dc}$, $I_{dc\,diode} = \dfrac{19.86\,mA_{dc}}{2}\,9.93\,mA_{dc}$, diode safe,

e. $PIV = 17.0\,V_p - 0.7\,V_p = 16.3\,V_p$, diode does not break down

18-10 **a.** $V_{p\,2} = 120\,V_{rms} \times \sqrt{2} \times \dfrac{1}{10} = 17\,V_p$, $V_{p\,out} = 17.0\,V_p - 1.4\,V = 15.6\,V_p$,

$I_{p\,out} = \dfrac{15.6\,V_p}{1\,k\Omega} = 15.6\,mA_p$, **b.** $f_{out} = 2 \times 60\,Hz = 120\,Hz$, $T = \dfrac{1}{120\,Hz} = 8.33\,ms$,

c. full-wave, 8.33 ms, 15.6 V$_p$; full-wave, 8.33 ms, 15.6 mA$_p$,

d. $I_{dc\,load} = \dfrac{2 \times \left(\dfrac{15.6\,v_p}{\pi} \right)}{1\,k\Omega} = 9.93\,mA_{dc}$, $I_{dc\,diode} = \dfrac{9.93\,mA_{dc}}{2} = 4.94\,mA_{dc}$, diode safe,

e. $PIV = 17.0\,V_p - 0.7\,V_p = 16.3\,V_p$, diode does not break down

18-11   a. $V_{p\,2} = 120\,V_{rms} \times \sqrt{2} \times \dfrac{1}{10} = 17\,V_p$, $V_{p\,out} = 17.0\,V_p - 1.4\,V = 15.6\,V_p$,

$I_{p\,out} = \dfrac{15.6\,V_p}{500\,\Omega} = 31.2\,mA_p$, **b.** $f_{out} = 2 \times 60\,Hz = 120\,Hz$, $T = \dfrac{1}{120\,Hz} = 8.33\,ms$,

c. 8.33 ms << 110 ms, 1.18 mV$_{pp}$, 341 mV$_{rms}$, **d.** $V_{min} = 15.6\,V_p\,(1 - 0.07575) = 14.4\,V_{min}$,

$V_{dc} = \left(\dfrac{15.6\,V_p + 14.4\,V_{min}}{2} \right) = 15\,V_{dc}$, **e.** triangle wave, 8.33 ms, 15.6 V$_p$, 14.4 V$_{min}$,

f. $\%\,ripple = \dfrac{341\,mV_{rms}}{15\,V_{dc}} \times 100\,\% = 2.3\,\%$ **g.** $PIV = 17.0\,V_p - 0.7\,V_p = 16.3\,V_p$, diode does not

break down

18-12   a. $V_{p\,2} = 120\,V_{rms} \times \sqrt{2} \times \dfrac{1}{10} = 17\,V_p$, $V_{p\,out} = 17.0\,V_p - 1.4\,V = 15.6\,V_p$,

$I_{p\,out} = \dfrac{15.6\,V_p}{500\,\Omega} = 15.6\,mA_p$, **b.** $f_{out} = 2 \times 60\,Hz = 120\,Hz$, $T = \dfrac{1}{120\,Hz} = 8.33\,ms$,

c. 8.33 ms << 220 ms, 590 mV$_{pp}$, 170 mV$_{rms}$, **d.** $V_{min} = 15.6\,V_p - 590\,mV_{pp} = 15.0\,V_{min}$,

$V_{dc} = \left(\dfrac{15.6\,V_p + 15\,V_{min}}{2} \right) = 15.3\,V_{dc}$, **e.** triangle wave, 8.33 ms, 15.6 V$_p$, 15.0 V$_{min}$,

f. $\%\,ripple = \dfrac{170\,mV_{rms}}{15.3\,V_{dc}} \times 100\,\% = 1.1\,\%$, **g.** $PIV = 17.0\,V_p - 0.7\,V_p = 16.3\,V_p$, diode does not

break down

18-13   a. $V_{dc\,out} = V_D = V_Z = 6.2\,V_{dc}$, $I_{dc\,out} = \dfrac{6.2\,V_{dc}}{500\,\Omega} = 12.4\,mA_{dc}$,

b. *Without load* & using I$_{Zmax}$: $R_{S\,min} = \dfrac{9.4\,V_{p\,RS}}{60\,mA_p} = 156\,\Omega$ (180 Ω is next standard highest value)

c. *Maximums* with load: $V_{p\,C} = 15.6\,V_p$, $V_{p\,RS} = 15.6\,V - 6.2\,V = 9.4\,V_p$,

$I_{p\,RS} = \dfrac{9.4\,V}{180\,\Omega} = 52.2\,mA_p$, $I_{p\,Z} = 52.2\,mA - 12.4\,mA_{dc} = 39.8\,mA_p$,

$P_{p\,RS} = 52.2\,mA \times 9.4\,V = 491\,mW_p$,

d. *Minimums* with load: $V_{pp\ ripple} = \dfrac{52.2\ mA}{120\ Hz \times 220\ \mu F} = 1.98\ V_{pp}$,

$V_{min\ C} = 15.6\ V_p - 1.98\ V_{pp} = 13.6\ V_{min}$, $V_{min\ RS} = 13.6\ V - 6.2\ V = 7.4\ V_{min}$,

$I_{min\ RS} = \dfrac{7.4\ V}{180\ \Omega} = 41.1\ mA_{min}$, $I_{min\ Z} = 41.1\ mA - 12.4\ mA = 28.7\ mA_{min}$ $(I_{Zmin}$ satisfied),

$P_{min\ RS} = 41.1\ mA \times 7.4\ V = 304\ mW_{min}$,

e. *Averages* with load: $V_{dc\ C} = \dfrac{15.6\ V_p + 13.6\ V_{min}}{2} = 14.6\ V_{dc}$,

$V_{dc\ RS} = \dfrac{9.4\ V_p + 7.4\ V_{min}}{2} = 8.4\ V_{dc}$, $I_{dc\ RS} = \dfrac{52.2\ mA_p + 41.1\ mA_{min}}{2} = 46.7\ mA_{dc}$,

$I_{dc\ Z} = \dfrac{39.8\ mA_p + 28.7\ mA_{min}}{2} = 34.3\ mA_{dc}$, $P_{RS\ avg} = \dfrac{491\ mW + 304\ mW}{2} = 398\ mW_{dc}$, select
at least a half-watt R_s

18-14   **a.** $V_{dc\ out} = V_p = V_Z = 6.2\ V_{dc}$, $I_{dc\ out} = \dfrac{6.2\ V_{dc}}{1\ k\Omega} = 6.2\ mA_{dc}$,

     b. *Without load* and using I_{Zmax}: $R_{S\ min} = \dfrac{9.4\ V_{p\ RS}}{60\ mA_p} = 156\ \Omega$ (180 is next standard highest value)

     c. *Maximums* with load: $V_{p\ C} = 15.6\ V_p$, $V_{p\ RS} = 15.6\ V - 6.2\ V = 9.4\ V_p$, $I_{p\ RS} = \dfrac{9.4\ V}{180\ \Omega} =$

     $52.2\ mA_p$, $I_{p\ Z} = 52.2\ mA - 6.2\ mA_{dc} = 46.0\ mA_p$, $P_{p\ RS} = 52.2\ mA \times 9.4\ V = 491\ mW_p$,

     d. *Minimums* with load: $V_{pp\ ripple} = \dfrac{52.2\ mA}{120\ Hz \times 220\ \mu F} = 1.98\ V_{pp}$,

$V_{min\ C} = 15.6\ V_p - 1.98\ V_{pp} = 13.6\ V_{min}$, $V_{min\ RS} = 13.6\ V - 6.2\ V = 7.4\ V_{min}$,

$I_{min\ RS} = \dfrac{7.4\ V}{180\ \Omega} = 41.1\ mA_{min}$, $I_{min\ Z} = 41.1\ mA - 6.2\ mA = 34.9\ mA_{min}$ $(I_{Zmin}$ satisfied),

$P_{min\ RS} = 41.1\ mA \times 7.4\ V = 304\ mW_{min}$,

     e. *Averages* with load: $V_{dc\ C} = \dfrac{15.6\ V_p + 13.6\ V_{min}}{2} = 14.6\ V_{dc}$,

$V_{dc\ RS} = \dfrac{9.4\ V_p + 7.4\ V_{min}}{2} = 8.4\ V_{dc}$, $I_{dc\ RS} = \dfrac{52.2\ mA_p + 41.1\ mA_{min}}{2} = 46.7\ mA_{dc}$,

$$I_{dc\,Z} = \frac{45.9\text{ mA}_p + 34.9\text{ mA}_{min}}{2} = 40.4\text{ mA}_{dc}, \quad P_{RS\,ave} = \frac{491\text{ mW} + 304\text{ mW}}{2} = 398\text{ mW}_{dc},$$

select at least a half-watt R_s

18-15 a. $V_{dc\,out} = 6.2\text{ V} - 0.8\text{ V}_{dc} = 5.4\text{ V}_{dc}, \quad I_{dc\,out} = \frac{5.4\text{ V}_{dc}}{20\ \Omega} = 270\text{ mA}_{dc},$

$P_{dc\,out} = 270\text{ mA}_{dc} \times 5.4\text{ V}_{dc} = 1.46\text{ W}_{dc},$ **b.** $I_B = \frac{270\text{ mA}_{dc}}{30} = 9\text{ mA}_{dc},$

c. $I_{Z\,min} = 30.0\text{ mA}_{min} - 9\text{ mA}_{dc} = 21\text{ mA}_{min}$ (I_{Zmin} satisfied)

d. $P_{BJT\,ave} = 270\text{ mA}_{dc} \times (14.95\text{ V}_{dc} - 5.4\text{ V}_{dc}) = 2.59\text{ W}_{dc},$ power dissipation okay but could heat sink to operate cooler

18-16 a. $V_{dc\,out} = 6.2\text{ V} - 0.8\text{ V}_{dc} = 5.4\text{ V}_{dc}, \quad I_{dc\,out} = \frac{5.4\text{ V}_{dc}}{10\ \Omega} = 540\text{ mA}_{dc},$

$P_{dc\,out} = 540\text{ mA}_{dc} \times 5.4\text{ V}_{dc} = 2.92\text{ W}_{dc},$ **b.** $I_B = \frac{540\text{ mA}_{dc}}{30} = 18\text{ mA}_p,$

c. $I_{Z\,min} = 30.0\text{ mA}_{min} - 18\text{ mA}_{dc} = 12\text{ mA}_{min}$ (I_{Zmin} satisfied),

d. $P_{BJT\,ave} = 540\text{ mA}_{dc} \times (14.95\text{ V}_{dc} - 5.4\text{ V}_{dc}) = 5.18\text{ W}_{dc},$ power dissipation okay but could heat sink to operate cooler

18-17 $A_{op\,amp} = \frac{1\text{ k}\Omega + 10\text{ k}\Omega}{10\text{ k}\Omega} = 1.10, \quad V_{out} = 1.10 \times 6.2\text{ V} = 6.82\text{ V}_{dc},$

$V_{out\,amp} = 1.5\text{ V} \times 6.82\text{ V}_{dc} = 8.32\text{ V}_{dc}, \quad I_{load} = \frac{6.82\text{ V}_{dc}}{15\ \Omega} = 455\text{ mA}_{dc},$

$I_{op\,amp\,out} = \frac{455\text{ mA}_{dc}}{100 \times 30} \, 152\ \mu\text{A}_{dc},$ rail voltage marginal

18-18 $R_f = 10\text{ k}\Omega \times 0.065 = 650\ \Omega$

18-19 $R_{limit} = \frac{0.7\text{ V}}{500\text{ mA}} = 1.4\ \Omega$

18-20 $R_{limit} = \frac{0.7\text{ V}}{250\text{ mA}} = 2.8\ \Omega$

18-21 $+A_{op\ amp} = \dfrac{49\ k\Omega + 100\ k\Omega}{100\ k\Omega} = 1.49,\ +V_{op\ amp\ out} = 1.10 \times 6.2\ V_{dc} = 9.24\ V_{dc},$

$-A_{op\ amp} = \dfrac{-100\ k\Omega}{100\ k\Omega} = -1.0,\ -V_{op\ amp\ out} = -1.0 \times 9.24\ V = -9.24\ V_{dc}$

18-22 $+A_{op\ amp} = \dfrac{49\ k\Omega + 100\ k\Omega}{100\ k\Omega} = 1.33,\ +V_{op\ amp\ out} = 1.10 \times 6.2\ V_{dc} = 8.25\ V_{dc},$

$-A_{op\ amp} = \dfrac{-100\ k\Omega}{100\ k\Omega} = -0.8,\ -V_{op\ amp\ out} = -1.0 \times 9.24\ V = -6.6\ V_{dc}$

18-23 **a.** $V_{dc\ out} = 12.0\ V_{dc},\ I_{out\ dc} = \dfrac{12.0\ V_{dc}}{25\ \Omega} = 480\ mA_{dc},\ P_{dc\ L} = 480\ mA_{dc} \times 12\ V_{dc} = 5.76\ W_{dc}$

b. $P_{ave} = 480\ mA_{dc} \times \left[\left(\dfrac{22\ V_{max} + 18\ V_{min}}{2}\right) - 12\ V_{dc}\right] = 3.84\ W_{dc},$

$T_J = 30\ {}^\circ C + \left(39\ {}^\circ C/W\right) \times 3.84\ W_{dc} = 180\ {}^\circ C$ **c.** No, $\Theta = \dfrac{100\ {}^\circ C - 30\ {}^\circ C}{3.84\ W_{dc}} = 18.2\ {}^\circ C/W$

d. $V_{pp\ ripple\ out} = \dfrac{22\ V_{max} - 18\ V_{min}}{10^4} = 0.4\ mV_{pp},\ 0.3\ \%$

18-24 **a.** $V_{dc\ out} = 12.0\ V_{dc},\ I_{dc\ out} = \dfrac{12\ V_{dc}}{35\ \Omega} = 343\ mA_{dc},\ P_{dc\ load} = 343\ mA_{dc} \times 12\ V_{dc} = 4.11\ W_{dc}$

b. $P_{ave} = 343\ mA_{dc} \times \left[\left(\dfrac{22\ V_{max} + 18\ V_{min}}{2}\right) - 12\ V_{dc}\right] = 2.74\ W_{dc},$

$T_J = 30^\circ C + \left(39^\circ C/W\right) \times 2.74\ W_{dc} = 137^\circ C$

c. No, $\Theta = \dfrac{100\ {}^\circ C - 30\ {}^\circ C}{2.74\ W_{dc}} = 21.4\ {}^\circ C/W$

d. $V_{pp\ ripple\ out} = \dfrac{22\ V_{max} - 18\ V_{min}}{10^4} = 0.4\ mV_{pp},\ 0.3\%$

18-25 **a.** $R_2 = \dfrac{3.75\ V_{dc}}{5.21\ mA_{dc}} = 720\ \Omega$ **b.** $I_{dc\ out} = 5.21\ mA_{dc} + 50\ mA_{dc} = 55\ mA_{dc}$

c. $P_{D \text{ ave}} = 55.21 \text{ mA}_{dc} \times (15 \text{ V}_{dc} - 5 \text{ V}_{dc}) = 552.1 \text{ mW}_{dc}$,

$T_J = 35 \,^{\circ}\text{C} + (160 \,^{\circ}\text{C/W}) \times 552.1 \text{ W}_{dc} = 123 \,^{\circ}\text{C}$ **d.** Yes but too close to specification, heat sinking recommended

18-26   a. $R_2 = \dfrac{8.75 \text{ V}_{dc}}{5.21 \text{ mA}_{dc}} = 1.68 \text{ k}\Omega$ **b.** $I_{out \ dc} = 5.21 \text{ mA}_{dc} + 100 \text{ mA}_{dc} = 105 \text{ mA}_{dc}$

c. $P_{D \text{ ave}} = 105.21 \text{ mA}_{dc} \times (15 \text{ V}_{dc} - 10 \text{ V}_{dc}) = 526 \text{ mW}_{dc}$,

$T_J = 35 \,^{\circ}\text{C} + (160 \,^{\circ}\text{C/W}) \times .526 \text{ mW}_{dc} = 119 \,^{\circ}\text{C}$ **d.** Yes, but operating close to specs, should use heat sink.

Chapter 19

19-1 $e_{source} = 8 \times 5 \text{ mV} = 40 \text{ mV}$ voltage source

19-2 $e_{source} = 10 \ \Omega \times 5 \text{ mA} = 50 \text{ mV}$ voltage source

19-3 $I_{source} = 10 \text{ mS} \times 5 \text{ mV} = 50 \ \mu\text{A}$ current source

19-4 $I_{source} = 10 \times 5 \text{ mA} = 50 \text{ mA}$ current source

19-5 $V_{\text{maximum of load}} = 20 \text{ V}_{rms}$ with open, $I_{\text{maximum of load}} = \dfrac{20 \text{ V}_{rms}}{4 \text{ k}\Omega} = 5 \text{ mA}_{rms}$ with short,

$P_{\text{maximum of load}} = \dfrac{4 \text{ k}\Omega}{(4 \text{ k}\Omega + 4 \text{ k}\Omega)^2} \times 20 \text{ V}_{rms} = 25 \text{ mW}$ with matched load of 4 kΩ

19-6 $V_{\text{maximum of load}} = 20 \text{ mA} \times 4 \text{ k}\Omega = 80 \text{ V}_{rms}$ with open, $I_{\text{maximum of load}} = 20 \text{ mA}_{rms}$ with short,

$P_{\text{maximum of load}} = \dfrac{4 \text{ k}\Omega}{(4 \text{ k}\Omega + 4 \text{ k}\Omega)^2} \times 80 \text{ V}_{rms} = 400 \text{ mW}$ with matched load of 4 kΩ

19-7   Maximum values with wiper arm at top: $V_{\text{maximum of load}} = 24 \text{ V}_p \left(\dfrac{6 \text{ k}\Omega // 12 \text{ k}\Omega}{6 \text{ k}\Omega // 12 \text{ k}\Omega + 12 \text{ k}\Omega} \right) = 6 \text{ V}_p$,

$I_{\text{maximum of load}} = \dfrac{6 \text{ V}_p}{6 \text{ k}\Omega} = 1 \text{ mA}_p$, $P_{\text{maximum of load}} = \dfrac{6 \text{ V}_p}{\sqrt{2}} \times \dfrac{1 \text{ mA}_p}{\sqrt{2}} = 3 \text{ mW}$; minimum values with

wiper arm at the bottom: $V_{\text{minimum of load}} = 0 \text{ V}$, $I_{\text{minimum of load}} = 0 \text{ A}$, $P_{\text{minimum of load}} = 0 \text{ W}$

19-8 $V_{\text{maximum of load}} = 24\ \text{V}_p \times \dfrac{6\ \text{k}\Omega}{6\ \text{k}\Omega + 6\ \text{k}\Omega + 12\ \text{k}\Omega} = 6\ \text{V with open,}$

$I_{\text{maximum of load}} = \dfrac{24\ \text{V}_p}{12\ \text{k}\Omega + 6\ \text{k}\Omega} = 1.33\ \text{mA}_p \text{ with short,}$

$P_{\text{maximum of load}} = \dfrac{6\ \text{V}_p^{\ 2}}{4.5\ \text{k}\Omega} = 2\ \text{mW with matched load of } 4.5\ \text{k}\Omega$

19-9 $V_{\text{out}} = 10 \times 100\ \text{mV}_{\text{rms}} = 1.0\ \text{V}_{\text{rms}}$, $I_{\text{out}} = \dfrac{1\ \text{V}_{\text{rms}}}{10\ \text{k}\Omega} = 0.1\ \text{mA}_{\text{rms}}$, ideal VCVS with dependent volt-

age source of $10 \times v_{\text{in}}$

19-10 $v_{\text{in}} = 100\ \text{mV}_{\text{rms}}\left(\dfrac{3\ \text{k}\Omega}{4\ \text{k}\Omega}\right) = 75\ \text{mV}_{\text{rms}}$, $V_{\text{out}} = -\dfrac{30\ \text{k}\Omega}{3\ \text{k}\Omega} \times 75\ \text{mV}_{\text{rms}} = 750\ \text{mV}_{\text{rms}}$, inverted

19-11 $S = 1 + \left(10^5 \times \dfrac{3\ \text{k}\Omega}{3\ \text{k}\Omega + 27\ \text{k}\Omega}\right) = 10001 \text{ (about } 10^4\text{)}$, $Z_{\text{in\_CL}} = 10^4 \times 2\ \text{M}\Omega = 20\ \text{G}\Omega$,

$Z_{\text{out\_CL}} = \dfrac{75\ \Omega}{10^4} = 7.5\ \text{m}\Omega$

19-12 VCVS model with $Z_{\text{in\_CL}} = 20\ \text{G}\Omega$, $A_{v\_CL} = \dfrac{10^5}{10{,}001} = 9.999$, $Z_{\text{out\_CL}} = 7.5\ \text{m}\Omega$;

$V_{\text{out\_CL}} = 100\ \text{mV}_{\text{rms}} \times \dfrac{20\ \text{G}\Omega}{100\ \text{k}\Omega + 20\ \text{G}\Omega} \times 9.999 \times \dfrac{10\ \text{k}\Omega}{10\ \text{k}\Omega + 7.5\ \text{m}\Omega} = 1\ \text{V}_{\text{rms}}$

Practically an ideal VCVS with dependent source of $10 \times v_{\text{in}}$ so ideally
$v_{\text{out}} = 10 \times 100\ \text{mV}_{\text{rms}} = 1\ \text{V}_{\text{rms}}$

19-13 $V_{\text{out\_1}} = -\left(10\ \text{k}\Omega \times 1\ \mu\text{A}_p\right) = -10\ \text{mV}_p$, $V_{\text{out\_2}} = -\left(\dfrac{-10\ \text{mV}_p}{10\ \text{k}\Omega}\right) = 10\ \text{mV}_p$

19-14 Inverting op amp with 30 kΩ feedback resistor converts to an ideal CCVS with dependent source of 30 k$\Omega \times i_{\text{in}}$ (still 750 mV$_{\text{rms}}$ output)

19-15 Ideal voltage to current converter op amp circuit with a 5 kΩ feedback resistor

19-16 $V_{\text{in}} = \dfrac{10\ \text{mA}}{20\ \text{mS}} = 0.5\ \text{V}$

19-17 $V_{out} = 0.8854 \times 500 \text{ mV}_{rms} = 443 \text{ mV}_{rms}$, $i_{out} = \dfrac{443 \text{ mV}_{rms}}{8 \text{ }\Omega} = 55.4 \text{ mA}_{rms}$,

$P_{out} = 443 \text{ mV}_{rms} \times 55.4 \text{ mA}_{rms} = 24.5 \text{ mW}$

19-18 $V_{out} = \dfrac{8 \text{ }\Omega}{10 \text{ }\Omega + 8 \text{ }\Omega} = 87.1 \text{ mV}_p$, $i_{out} = \dfrac{87.1 \text{ mV}_p}{8 \text{ }\Omega} = 10.9 \text{ mA}_p$,

$P_{ave \text{ } out} = \dfrac{87.1 \text{ mV}_p}{\sqrt{2}} \times \dfrac{10.88 \text{ mA}_p}{\sqrt{2}} = 475 \text{ }\mu W$

19-19 Ideal current amplifier op amp circuit with $R_f = 99 \text{ } R_i$ (one design: an R_i value of 1 kΩ and an R_f value of 99 kΩ)

19-20 The input signal is decreased from 120 mV$_{rms}$ to 100 V$_{rms}$, thus

$V_{out2} = V_{out1} = \left(\dfrac{100 \text{ mV}_p}{120 \text{ mV}_p} \right) 60.99 \text{ mV}_p = 50.8 \text{ mV}_p$

19-21 $I_{C Q1} = I_{C Q2} = 1.0 \text{ mA}_{dc}$, $I_{E Q3} = I_{E Q4} = \dfrac{1 \text{ mA}_{dc}}{2} = 0.5 \text{ mA}_{dc}$, $\beta_{DP} = 150 \times 150 = 22,500$,

$r'_{e\_DP} = 2 \left(\dfrac{26 \text{ mV}}{0.5 \text{ mA}} + 0.5 \text{ }\Omega \right) = 108 \text{ }\Omega$, $r_{input} = (22,500) \times 108 \text{ }\Omega = 2.4 \text{ M}\Omega$;

single BJT: $r'_{e\_BJT} = \dfrac{26 \text{ mV}}{0.5 \text{ mA}} + 0.5 \text{ }\Omega = 54 \text{ }\Omega$, $z_{in\_BJT} = 150 (54 \text{ }\Omega) = 8.1 \text{ k}\Omega$

comparison: significant increase of 300 in input impedance into the MΩ range, voltage gain cut in half since r_C remains the same but r'_{e_DP} is double r'_{e_BJT}.

19-22 Signal: $V_{out} = 30 \times 100 \text{ mV}_p = 3 \text{ V}_p$ signal,

Noise: $20 \log(CMRR) = 60 \text{ dB}$, $CMRR = 10^3$, $A_{v\_CM} = \dfrac{30}{10^3} = 0.03$,

$v_{out\_CM} = 0.03 \left(10 \text{ mV}_{p \text{ noise in}} \right) = 0.3 \text{ mV}_{p \text{ noise out}}$, $signal - to - noise \text{ } ratio = \dfrac{3 \text{ mV}_p}{0.3 \text{ mV}_p} = 10$

Chapter 20

20-1 omitted

20-2 omitted

20-3 The gain is cut in half

20-4 The gain is half of the programmed setting

20-5

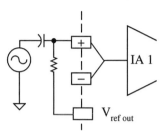

20-6 omitted

20-7 See Figure 20-8. The gain for IA1 = 8. The gain for IA2 = 2.

20-8 See Figure 20-10. The gain for IA1=8. The gain for IA2=2.

20-9

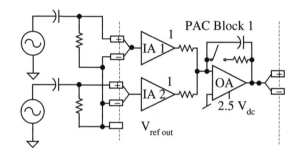

20-10 Disconnect $V_{\text{ref out}}$ from question 20-9 and connect the removed wires to an external reference voltage. Leave $V_{\text{ref out}}$ unconnected.

20-11 Figure 20-13. $R_f = 4R_i = 328$ kΩ, pick 330 kΩ, $R_i = \dfrac{R_f}{4} = 82$ kΩ

20-12 Figure 20-13

20-13   Figure 20-16; $R_f = 4R_i = 328$ kΩ, pick 330 kΩ, $R_i = .2$ $R_f = \dfrac{R_f}{4} = 82$ kΩ,

$$\beta = \frac{82 \text{ k}\Omega}{82 \text{ k}\Omega + 330 \text{ k}\Omega} = 0.2, \text{ pick } R = 620 \text{ k}\Omega, \quad C = \frac{50 \text{ } \mu sec}{2 \times 620 \text{ k}\Omega \times 1n\left(\dfrac{1+0.2}{1-0.2}\right)} = 100 \text{ pF}$$

20-14   Figure 20-16. $\beta = \dfrac{120 \text{ k}\Omega}{82 \text{ k}\Omega + 120 \text{ k}\Omega} = 0.594$, pick R=620 kΩ,

$$C = \frac{1}{440 \text{ Hz} \times 2 \times 620 \text{ k}\Omega \times 1 \text{ n}\left(\dfrac{1+0.594}{1-0.594}\right)} = 1.34 \text{ nF}$$

20-15   omitted

20-16   omitted

20-17   See Example 20-3, V+ = 5 V_{dc}, V− = −5 V_{dc}, $C_t = 2.2$ nF, $R_t = 2.2$ kΩ to pin 7, FSK pin to common or V+, $R_{pull\text{-}up} = 5.6$ kΩ

20-18   omitted

20-19   See Example 20-4, V+ = 5 V_{dc}, V− = −5V_{dc}, $C_t = 1$ μF, $R_t = 9.1$ kΩ, 180 Ω pin 13 to pin 14, $R_{mult} = 8.8$ kΩ

20-20   omitted

20-21   See Example 20-5, $R_{mult} = 18$ kΩ. Place a 820 Ω resistor between the control voltage and the AM pin (pin 1). Place a 3.3 kΩ resistor between the AM pin (pin 1) and common.

20-22   omitted